ANATOMY
for
Funeral Service

1st Edition

Published by

PROFESSIONAL TRAINING SCHOOLS, INC.
4722 Bronze Way   Dallas, Texas 75236

Table of Contents

PURPOSE AND OBJECTIVES

This section on human anatomy is intended to introduce the student of mortuary science to the basic, introductory concepts and terminology associated with the study of the human body. Anatomy is one of the major areas of scientific study required of mortuary science students, and the material learned serves as an important base of knowledge for the understanding and learning of additional course work in areas such as pathology, embalming, restorative art, and microbiology.

As professional funeral directors and embalmers, students will eventually be in the position of dealing directly and indirectly with other members of the allied health professions, such as doctors, nursing personnel, and medical technicians. It is desirable that students of mortuary science have an understanding of basic anatomical terminology in order to be able to effectively communicate with these professionals, as well as with the families they serve and the general public.

An understanding of human anatomy is also important in developing a sense of respect for the dead human remains, which is critical to the successful emergence of professionals in the funeral service field. Not only should a respect for the dead be developed, but the human body should be appreciated as a subject for independent study and continued intellectual growth.

In addition, it is hoped that through learning basic human anatomy, and becoming familiar with the body's various systems, students will better understand the relationship between structure and function of the human body. Meeting this objective will hopefully foster the development of healthful living habits as a result of being more aware of the intricate nature of the body in which we live.

INTRODUCTION TO ANATOMY
Chapter 1

Anatomy is an ancient science. Doctors and scientists have been studying the human body for hundreds of years. It must be remembered when studying human anatomy, that many of the words used in describing the body have been derived from the old Latin and Greek languages. Thus, an understanding of basic word meanings can be of great help in realizing how or why many terms associated with the study of the human body were originally developed. For example, the word anatomy comes from the Greek language meaning "throughout" and "to cut". In other words, the body has been scientifically studied over the years by cutting it up in order to better understand its structure. Therefore, we normally define the word anatomy as the study of the structure of the body.

Anatomy is a very broad science, and it is often beneficial to look at its subdivisions in order to better understand the overall field of anatomy. **Gross anatomy** refers to the study of the body with the unaided eye. Observations may be made without the aid of a microscope. **Microscopic anatomy, or histology**, refers to the study of the body with the aid of a microscope. The term "histo-" means tissue, and the suffix "-ology" means the study or science of something. Therefore, histology is literally the study of the tissues in the body, which can only be effectively accomplished with the aid of magnification supplied by the use of a microscope. Closely associated with histology is **cytology**, which refers to the study of individual cells. **Systemic anatomy** is the study of individual body organs and systems, such as the study of the digestive system, or the study of the respiratory system. **Regional anatomy** is the study of some particular body region as a separate unit, such as the study of the head, or the study of the chest area. **Developmental anatomy**, or **embryology**, refers to the study of the body before birth, from its earliest beginnings as a fertilized egg, until the time of birth. **Pathological anatomy**, or **human pathology**, is concerned with studying the structural and functional changes which occur in the body as a result of disease. **Topographical anatomy**, or surface anatomy, refers to the study of surface shape and form of the human body, and the ability to use this knowledge of surface form to locate underlying structures.

While anatomy refers to the study of the structure of the body, **human physiology** would be concerned with the study of the function of the body and its parts. It should soon become apparent that the fields of anatomy and physiology are intimately related. The various parts of the human body are structured in a precise manner in order to be able to perform their respective functions. Therefore, it is not hard to imagine that whenever the structure of a body part is altered by disease, its function is likely to be affected accordingly.

Body Organization

The first level of organization in the human body occurs at a chemical level. This level includes all of the atoms and molecules which come together to form the various chemical substances necessary to maintain life as we know it. Protoplasm is a highly specialized product that is a combination of various chemical elements organized into units known as cells. *(See Fig. 1)* Cells are the smallest, functional units of organization in the body, and are said to possess the somewhat magical "qualities of life". In other words, it is at the cellular level where we can first observe these special characteristics:

1. irritability, or the ability to respond to a stimulus

2. the ability to take in food and water

3. the ability to give off waste products

4. the ability to grow and mature

5. the ability to reproduce

The ability to take in food and water, and the ability to give off waste products, collectively describe the basic process of metabolism. The term metabolism refers to the sum total of all the chemical reactions which occur at the cellular level in the body. It includes the breaking down of food products which have been digested and taken into the cell, with the release of energy, and the resulting ability of the cell to perform work. This work includes the building of food molecules into more complex compounds, which in turn serves as the basis for maintenance of bodily functions and the growth of new cells.

1. **Nucleus** - controls most cellular activities, including reproduction, protein synthesis, and contains the cell's genetic material which determines a person's various characteristics

2. **Cytoplasm** - the protoplasm of a cell which lies between the nucleus and the cell membrane - contains numerous small structures, or "organelles", which perform various cellular activities, such as:

    A. **ribisomes** - synthesize proteins

    B. **mitochondria** - cellular "power plants" which produce energy

    C. **lysosomes** - contain enzymes which digest substances brought into the cell

    D. **endoplasmic reticulum** - series of membranes forming canals which transport nutrients and other materials through the cell

    E. **centrioles** - important in cell division/reproduction

3. **Plasma (Cell) Membrane** - forms the outer boundary of the cell - keeps the cell intact, and regulates the passage of fluids and other substances in and out of the cell - because only certain substances can enter and leave, it is sometimes described as a "semi-permeable" membrane

The next level of organization, after the cellular level, is recognized as the **tissues** of the body. The term tissue refers to a group of similar cells arranged for the performance of some particular function. For example, a group of similar muscle cells join together to help create movement, or a group of cells may have the function of holding together, or supporting, certain parts of the body. It is generally recognized that the tissues of the body may be subdivided into four main categories.

Epithelial tissue is that general category of tissue which is found covering the outer surface of many body parts and lining the inner surfaces of body cavities and organs. It is also the variety of tissue which is involved in forming secretions produced by many glands in the body.

A **membrane** is any thin, sheet-like expanse of tissue, and many body membranes are epithelial in nature. For example, the outer layer of the skin, or epidermis, and the mucous membranes lining the respiratory and digestive tracts, are epithelial tissues. Mucous membranes line body cavities which open out on the surface of the body, and secrete mucous, which is a thick, slippery substance that helps keep the body parts moist and soft. Another type of epithelial membrane is the serous membrane, which lines closed body cavities, such as the inside of the chest or abdominal areas. These membranes secrete serum. Serum serves as a slick, lubricating substance, and helps reduce friction between moving body parts. Epithelial tissue is also distinguished by the fact that the individual cells are packed closely together, with little intercellular substance between them. The cells also appear in a variety of shapes, such as flat (squamous), tall and narrow (columnar), or square (cuboidal) cells. They may also appear in layers, in which case they are referred to as "stratified" epithelium.

The second main category of tissue in the body is **connective** tissue. Connective tissue basically serves the purpose of protecting, supporting, and binding body parts together. As opposed to epithelial tissues, the individual cells are generally not as close together, and there is more inert, intercellular substance between the cells. There is a great variety of connective tissue in the body, some of it appearing in a delicate, web-like arrangement, tough fibers, solid or rigid tissue, or even in fluid form. Following is a list of the most common forms of connective tissue:

1. areolar (loose) connective tissue - a variety of scattered, irregular fibers embedded in a soft, gel-like base (hyaluronic acid) - it serves as the "glue" which underlies and binds together many other body tissues

2. adipose (fatty) tissue - a type of connective tissue specialized for storing fat

3. fibrous connective tissue - strong, fibrous bundles of tissue, which provide great strength and support - includes tendons, ligaments, and fascia

4. bone - hardened, calcified connective tissue

5. cartilage - made up of a softer, more flexible consistency than bone

6. hemopoietic (blood forming) tissue, and the blood itself - specialized tissue found in red bone marrow, and in such areas as the spleen, tonsils, and lymph nodes - blood is unusual in that it is a liquid connective tissue

Muscle tissue is another main category of body tissue, and is responsible for the movement of body parts. Muscle tissue will be discussed in more detail in a later chapter.

The fourth main category of body tissue is **nervous** tissue. It makes up the various parts of the nervous system, which has to do with receiving stimuli, conducting impulses, and having overall control of the various bodily functions. Nervous tissue is also discussed later in the chapter on the nervous system.

Just as tissues were defined as an arrangement of cells, **organs** may be described as a group of tissues arranged for the performance of some function. For example, muscle cells make up muscular tissue, and muscle tissue is arranged into independent organs, called muscles, whose function is to impart movement to various body parts. Organs may have two or more types of tissue in them, which ultimately allows for the performance of more specialized functions than one type of tissue alone could manage.

The next higher level of body organization is the **system** level. A system is a group of organs arranged for the performance of some particular function. Continuing with our use of muscles as an example, all of the independent muscular organs in the body, taken together, would constitute the muscular system. The entire muscular system is capable of performing more complex functions than single muscular organs. Following is a list of the major systems in the human body:

1. skeletal system - the bones, cartilage, and ligaments which provide support and protection to the body

2. circulatory system - the heart, blood, and blood vessels, plus the lymphatic system, serving to transport gases, nutrients, and waste products throughout the body, plus helping to protect it against disease

3. muscular system - all of the body's muscles which are concerned primarily with movement of body parts

4. endocrine system - the group of glands which give off secretions which serve as chemical regulators of various bodily functions

5. nervous system - the brain, spinal cord, and nerves which have overall control over bodily functions, and serve to coordinate the performance of tasks by various cells, tissue, and organs in the body

6. digestive system - the various organs concerned with the taking in of food products, breaking them down so nutrients can be absorbed, and the elimination of solid waste products

7. urinary system - the kidneys and related organs which serve to clean waste products from the blood and maintain proper fluid and chemical balances in the body

8. respiratory system - the lungs and other organs concerned with taking in oxygen and the elimination of other respiratory gases

9. reproductive system - those organs, both male and female, which are involved in reproduction of the species and the development of sexual characteristics

10. integumentary system - the skin and its components which are involved in covering and protecting the body as a whole, as well as such functions as temperature regulation and acting as a sensory organ

Each of these body systems, when taken together, make up the entire organism known as the human body.

The concept of the anatomical position is important in serving as a reference upon which a common understanding of other concepts and terminology is based. In other words, it is helpful when trying to use and learn terminology which describes the human body to have everyone thinking of the body as being in the same position. When we are all thinking along the same lines, describing the body and its parts becomes much easier. The anatomical position always assumes that the body is standing erect, facing the observer, with the arms at the sides, and the palms of the hands turned forward. It is important to keep this picture of the body in mind as we discuss additional terms referring to position and direction. *(See Fig. 2)*

In studying the human body, it is often useful to divide the body or its parts into subdivisions or sections. In order to do this, we make use of certain imaginary lines, or **planes**, which cut the body into different parts. *(See Fig. 3)* First is the **sagittal plane**, which cuts the body from front to back, resulting in right and left parts. There are any possible number of sagittal planes, but only one sagittal plane would be exactly in the middle and cut the body into equal halves. This sagittal plane is called the **mid-sagittal**, or **median plane**. Closely associated with the concept of the median plane is the idea of **bi-lateral symmetry**. This concept refers to the fact that the median plane, and only the median plane, divides the body into two equal or symmetrical halves.

A **frontal, or coronal plane**, is a vertical plane which cuts the body from side to side, at right angles to the median plane, and results in front and back parts of the body.

A **horizontal, transverse, or cross plane,** is one which cuts the body horizontally, or crosswise, and results in upper and lower body parts.

Directional Terms

Following is a list of directional terms which are important and useful in describing the relative location and positions of various bodily structures.

1. **medial** and **lateral** - the term medial refers to something which is located toward the midline, or median plane of the body, while lateral refers to a location away from the median plane, or toward the sides of the body (or body part).

2. **superior, cranial,** or **cephalic,** and **inferior** or **caudal** - the terms superior, cranial, and cephalic refer to something located toward the head, or upper part of the body, whereas inferior or caudal refer to the "tail", or lower part of the body.

3. **anterior** or **ventral,** and **posterior** or **dorsal** - anterior and ventral are used to mean toward the front of the body, while posterior and dorsal mean toward the back of the body.

4. **deep, central,** or **internal** - these terms refer to something which is located toward the interior, or center of the body (or body part), and away from the surface.

5. **superficial, external,** or **peripheral** - these terms mean toward the surface, or edges of the body or body part

6. **visceral** - visceral is a term used to refer to the organs contained within the body cavities.

7. **parietal** - parietal is used to refer to the walls of a body cavity.

8. **proximal** and **distal** - proximal is a term referring to something which is located toward or closer to the point of attachment of a limb to the trunk of the body, and distal means farther away from the point of attachment of a limb to the trunk.

9. **prone** and **supine** - prone refers to a position of the body when it is lying face down, and supine when it is lying face up. The terms are also used to describe the position of the hands when they are turned palms up (supine) or palms down (prone).

Gross Anatomy

The human body is often subdivided into several main parts for the purpose of anatomical study, and the terms used in reference to these body regions are used throughout the study of anatomy. The first gross subdivision is the **head**, which in turn may be subdivided into **cranium** and **face**. When we approach the study of the skeletal system, we will better see exactly which bones are included in the cranium and which are in the face. The second subdivision is the neck area, or **cervical** region. Third is the **trunk** or **torso**, which includes the **thorax, abdomen,** and **pelvis.** The fourth overall subdivision of the body is the **upper extremities,** which includes the arms and the pectoral girdle, or the shoulder blades and collar bones. Fifth is the **lower extremities,** which includes the legs and the pelvic girdle, or hip bones.

Also important in studying gross anatomy of the human body are the body cavities, which contain various body organs. The dorsal cavity is a main body cavity which is made up of the cranial cavity within the skull, containing the brain, and the spinal cavity within the vertebral column, containing the spinal cord. The **ventral** cavity is the large cavity contained within the trunk of the body. It in turn contains the following subdivisions:

A. **thoracic cavity** - the upper part of the torso or trunk, within the chest area. Found within the thoracic cavity are the:

    1. **pleural cavities** - the spaces around the lungs, between the two layers of pleura, which are serous membranes covering over each lung

    2. **pericardial cavity** - the space around the heart, between the two layers of pericardium, which is a "sac-like" structure covering the heart

    3. **mediastinal cavity (mediastinum)** - the area in the center of the thorax, from the base of the neck to the diaphragm, and in-between the lungs

B. **abdominopelvic cavity** - that part of the ventral cavity below the diaphragm. Although no wall separates the two, it may in turn be sub-divided into the:

    1. **abdominal cavity** - the upper part of the abdominopelvic cavity, below the diaphragm and down to approximately the top of the hip bones

    2. **pelvic cavity** - the lower part of the abdominopelvic cavity, contained within the pelvis

Also contained within the abdominopelvic cavity is the **peritoneal cavity**. The peritoneum, like the pleura and pericardium, is a two-layered serous membrane. It covers over and around many of the organs in the abdominopelvic cavity, holding them in place and transmitting nerves and vessels. Like the pleura and pericardium, it secretes serous fluid which helps to lubricate and moisten the parts it comes in contact with. In addition, it lines the inside walls of the cavity, and the space between its two layers may be referred to as the peritoneal cavity.

Other body cavities include the **oral** or **buccal cavity** within the mouth, the **nasal cavity** within the nose, and the **orbital cavities**, or **eyesockets**, containing the eyes.

Surface / Topographical Anatomy

Several concepts related to surface form of the body, and corresponding underlying structures, are of particular importance to students of mortuary science. The first of these is the idea of a **linear guide**. A linear guide may be defined as an imaginary line drawn on the surface of the body which represents the approximate location of some deeper, underlying structure. Being able to envision an imaginary line drawn on the surface of a dead human body, from one point to another point, can assist the embalmer in deciding where to make an incision in order to locate a vessel to be used for the embalming operation. An **anatomical guide** may be defined as any surface, prominence, or structure which is used in locating an adjacent structure or prominence. In other words, one piece of anatomy is used as a guide in finding another piece of anatomy, such as a blood vessel. The third concept is that of **anatomical limits**. This refers to the point of origin and the point of termination of a structure, such as a blood vessel, in relation to adjacent anatomical structures. In other words, a blood vessel may be coursing through the body, and when it passes a certain point, such as a bone, it changes names. The vessel may continue along, eventually passing another structure, such as a muscle, and it changes names again. In this instance, the bone and the muscle could be described as the anatomical limits of the blood vessel in question.

To illustrate these concepts, let's consider the right common carotid artery as an example. An embalmer learns that drawing an imaginary line (linear guide) from the sternoclavicular articulation to the lobe of the ear will help locate the underlying common carotid artery. The embalmer will also learn that this same vessel may be located along the medial border of the sternocleidomastoideus muscle (anatomical guide), and that the right common carotid artery originates behind the sternoclavicular articulation and terminates at the superior border of the thyroid cartilage (anatomical limits).

Regional Anatomy

Although most introductory courses in human anatomy are approached systemically, there are several important concepts relating to regional anatomy which will be discussed in this and additional chapters. To facilitate the location of abdominal viscera, it is often helpful to divide the abdominal-pelvic area into nine separate regions, identified as follows: *(See Fig. 4)*

1. hypochondriac regions - the superior, lateral regions

2. epigastric region - the superior, middle region

3. umbilical region - the middle region, around the navel area

4. lumbar regions - the regions immediately lateral to the umbilical region

5. iliac/inguinal regions - the inferior, lateral regions

6. hypogastric region - the inferior, middle region

Another, more simplified way to view the abdominal-pelvic area is through the use of the four region plan. This plan simply divides the area into four quadrants by drawing a vertical (mid-sagittal) and horizontal line which intersect in the navel area. The resulting quadrants are then referred to as the upper right, upper left, lower right, and lower left quadrants.

Additional concepts related to the regional study of the human body are the anterior cervical triangle and the femoral triangle. *(See Figs. 25 & 26)* These are triangular shaped regions located, respectively, in the front of the neck area and the upper, anterior femoral region. Each will be discussed in more detail in the chapter on muscles. Table A is a listing of other important terms which are used to identify various regions of the body.

TABLE A

Abdominal - the area in the front of the trunk, below the diaphragm

Antecubital - the depression just in front of the elbow joint

Axillary - the armpit area

Brachial - the arm

Buccal or oral - the mouth

Calf - the posterior, lower leg

Carpal - the wrist

Cephalic - the head

Cervical - the neck

Cranial - the skull

Cutaneous - the skin

Digital - the fingers or toes

Facial - the face

Femoral - the thigh, or upper leg

Gluteal - the buttocks

Groin or inguinal - the area where the thigh meets the trunk

Lumbar - the lower back, between the ribs and hip bones

Nasal - the nose

Occipital - the lower back of the skull

Optic, Ophthalmic, or Orbital - the eyes

Palmar - the palm of the hand

Pelvic - the lower part of the trunk

Plantar - the sole of the foot

Popliteal - the knee area

Pubic - the genital region

Tarsal - the ankle

Temporal - the sides of the skull

Thoracic - the chest area

Umbilical - the navel area

THE SKIN - INTEGUMENTARY SYSTEM
Chapter 2

Surrounding our body is a layer of material that we call our skin. Our skin and those structures closely related to it are called the **integumentary** system or the **cutaneous membrane** (actually a misnomer for the skin).

Functions of the Skin

Our skin has several functions. It acts as a protective covering for the body helping to keep foreign objects out as well as those entities which belong inside the body in. Through the process of sweating it helps to regulate and maintain body temperature. Sweating will also function to help eliminate certain body wastes. As the first thing that comes in contact with our surroundings, it serves as a bed for sensory nerve receptors, allowing us to feel and touch as well as to sense heat and cold.

Factors Which Influence Skin Color

There are various factors that have a bearing on our skin color, the most obvious being the amount, color, and distribution of pigments in our skin. This is a hereditary characteristic that we receive from our parents. Another characteristic that we might inherit is the number of superficial vessels that allow blood to be very close to the surface of the skin. If you have ever been embarrassed, you sensed the warmth of your skin as you turned red when these superficial vessels dilated, allowing additional blood closer to the surface. Your own state of health can have an effect on your skin color. Has someone ever said that you look pale when you were sick? Your age can also help to determine your skin color. Infants are sure to have some changes in skin color as they grow into childhood, much like an old person may undergo slight changes in skin color as they get older. Where you live and what type of activities you participate in can also affect your skin color due to climatic conditions. One who works outside, or is active in outdoor sports, will have a different color compared to someone who rarely goes outside.

Skin Layers

The skin is made up of two (2) primary layers. The epidermis is the outer (external) primary layer of skin. It is composed primarily of epithelial tissue laying on top of a layer of connective tissue. The internal primary layer of the skin is called the dermis and it is primarily connective tissue. *(See Fig. 5)*

The epidermis contains melanin cells which are the brownish-black pigments of the skin. The absence of these cells is called albinism, (the individual, an albino). Freckles are due to concentrations of melanin. Other related structures of the epidermis are hair and nails. Hair is an outgrowth of the epidermis. The hair follicle is the cylindrical cavity containing the root, and the shaft of the hair extends above the surface of the skin. The nails of the fingers and toes are specialized epidermal cells.

The dermis is the inner (internal) primary layer of the skin. It is composed primarily of connective tissue. The dermis contains small blood vessels, lymph vessels, and nerves of the skin. Other related structures of the dermis are the sebaceous glands (or oil glands), which secrete sebum and serve to keep the hair and skin soft and pliable. The sudoriferous glands (or sweat glands) secrete sudor, and are found on most body surfaces. They open onto the surface of the skin through tiny openings called pores. The ceruminous glands (or "ear wax glands") secrete cerumen which helps to protect the ear canal by trapping bacteria and foreign particles. However, excess accumulations of cerumen can block the passage of sound waves entering the auditory canal.

THE SKELETAL SYSTEM
Chapter 3

The skeletal system consists mainly of two important types of connective tissues - cartilage and bone. *(See Fig. 6)* In an embryo, the skeleton is mainly cartilage in nature, and by adulthood, most of this cartilage has been replaced by hardened bone. Cartilage continues to exist, however, in certain areas of the body such as the nose, outer ear, voicebox, and at points where bones attach to one another. Like other connective tissues, bone contains functional cells, called osteocytes, and a great deal of intercellular material. However, unlike other connective tissues, in bone most of this intercellular material becomes hardened by the deposition of mineral salts, especially calcium. This is a gradual process which occurs over a period of years, until a person's bones become fully developed into their normal adult form. This process of bone formation is called ossification. Even after bone has reached its normal state of "hardness", activity does not cease within bone tissue. Bones are dynamic organs, and have the ability to continually maintain and repair themselves throughout life.

Structure of Bone

The outer layer, or shell, of a bone is usually quite dense in nature, and is referred to as **compact bone.** *(See Fig. 20)* Although it is called compact bone, it nevertheless contains an intricate, structural arrangement of circular rings of tissue containing bone cells, hardened intercellular substances, and numerous minute canals for blood vessels. These complex structural units are referred to as **Haversian systems.**

The interior part of most bones consists of a more "spongy", or porous type of bone, which is referred to as **cancellous bone.** It contains many spaces that are occupied by red bone marrow, which is responsible for the manufacture of blood cells in the body. In addition, bones are covered with a tough, outer membrane called the **periosteum.** A long bone is made up of the diaphysis, or shaft, the epiphyses, or ends of the bone, the articular cartilage, which covers and cushions the ends of bones where they form a joint, and the medullary canal or cavity, containing yellow bone marrow.

Functions of Bone

The basic functions of bone can generally be summarized into five main areas, as follows:

1. Support - bone provides support and rigidity to the soft tissues of the body so that our normal, erect posture can be maintained.

2. Protection - bones help to protect the more delicate, vital organs which they surround, such as the protection provided to the brain by the bones of the cranium.

3. Movement - bones serve as levers, or points of attachment for the body's muscles, which pull on the bones and result in movement.

4. Storage - bones serve as warehouses, or storage areas, for important minerals in the body, such as calcium. When blood calcium levels rise above normal, the calcium moves into the bones and is stored. When calcium levels in the blood fall, some stored calcium leaves the bones and enters the bloodstream to be used throughout the body.

5. Hemopoiesis - this term is a combination to the Greek words "hemo", meaning blood, and "poiesis", meaning to make or manufacture. Blood cell production occurs primarily in the red bone marrow of the body.

TABLE B
Outline of the Skeleton

	Number of Bones
I. Axial Skeleton	
A. Skull	28
1. cranium	8
2. face	14
3. ear bones	6
B. Hyoid Bone	1
C. Vertebrae	26
D. Ribs	24
E. Sternum	1
Total Axial	**80**
II. Appendicular Skeleton	
A. Upper Extremity/Pectoral Girdle	
1. scapula	2
2. clavicle	2
3. humerus	2
4. radius	2
5. ulna	2
6. carpals	16
7. metacarpals	10
8. phalanges	28
Total Upper Extremity	**64**
B. Lower Extremity/Pelvic Girdle	
1. os coxa	2
2. femur	2
3. patella	2
4. tibia	2
5. fibula	2
6. tarsals	14
7. metatarsals	10
8. phalanges	28
Total Lower Extremity	**62**
Total Appendicular	**126**
Total Axial	**80**
Total in the Body	**206**

14

TABLE C
Bony Landmarks

Antrum or Sinus - An air cavity within a bone

Canal or Meatus - a tunnel-like passageway or opening in a bone

Condyle - a smooth, curved articular surface on a bone

Crest - a prominent ridge on a bone

Epicondyle - a prominence just above a condyle

Fissure - a narrow slit or groove in a bone

Fontanel - a temporarily unossified area between the cranial bones of an infant

Foramen - a hole in a bone

Fossa - a depression in a bone

Head - a ball-like articular projection on a bone

Process - any prominent projection or outgrowth of bone

Septum - a wall or partition which divides a body cavity

Tubercle or Tuberosity - a bump or elevation on a bone

Divisions of the Skeleton

The human skeleton consists of 206 classified bones, and they are generally grouped into two main subdivisions, called the axial and appendicular skeletons. Classified bones are those which are always present in the normal human body. The axial skeleton includes all of the bones of the skull, the hyoid bone, the thorax, and the spine. The appendicular skeleton includes the bones of the upper extremities and pectoral girdle (arms, wrists, hands, fingers, collar bones, and shoulder blades), plus the bones of the lower extremities and pelvic girdle (legs, ankles, feet, toes, and hip bones). *(See Figs. 6 & 7)*

Besides the 206 classified bones of the body, there are two other recognized types of bones, which are very irregular, and may or may not be present in a given individual. The first of these "unclassified" bones are called **sutural bones,** which are small, chip-like pieces of bones sometimes found embedded between the cranial bones. The points at which the cranial bones meet are referred to as sutures. The other type of unclassified bones are called **sesamoid bones.** The word sesamoid literally means "resembling a sesame seed". By definition, these small, variable bones are occasionally found embedded in tendons, most often at points where pressure exists, such as where a tendon moves over a bony prominence. The kneecaps are exceptions in that they develop in, and are surrounded by tendon, but are present in all bodies; thus they are classified sesamoid bones.

Axial Skeleton

The **skull**, which contains 28 bones, may be subdivided into three categories: the cranium, the face, and the ear bones. *(See Figs. 8, 9, 10, 11)*

The **cranium** consists of eight bones which form the cranial cavity and which house the brain.

1. The **frontal** bone forms the forehead area, the front, top of the cranium, and the upper part of the eyesockets. Important landmarks of the frontal bone include the **supraorbital margins,** or the upper rim of the eyesockets, the **superciliary arches,** which are elevations at and above the medial ends of the eyebrows, the **glabella,** which is a prominence just above the nasal bones, between the medial ends of the eyebrows, and the **frontal eminences,** which are described as gently rounded prominences at the upper border of the forehead. Also contained within the frontal bone are the **frontal sinuses,** which are cavities that communicate with the nasal passages. *(See Fig. 9)*

2. The **parietal bones** form the majority of the upper sides and top of the cranium. *(See Fig. 9)*

3. The **temporal bones** form the lower sides of the cranium, basically surrounding the ears. The upper flat portion, adjacent to the parietal bones, is called the **squama.** The inferior, or petrous portion, includes the hearing canal, and houses the tiny ear bones. The **zygomatic process** is a projection on the temporal bone which extends forward, anterior to the hearing canal, to unite with the cheek bone. The **mastoid process** is a prominent projection on the inferior part of the temporal bone, just behind the lobe of the ear. The **external auditory meatus**, or hearing canal, is a tunnel in the temporal bone which extends medially from the external ear to the middle ear. The **mandibular fossa** is a depression on the temporal bone, just anterior to the external auditory meatus, which articulates with the condyles of the lower jaw. The **carotid canal** is a passageway in the temporal bone through which the internal carotid artery passes in taking blood to the brain. *(See Fig. 9)*

4. The **occipital bone** makes up the lower back part of the cranium. The large opening in the inferior portion of the occipital bone, through which the spinal cord passes to connect to the brain, is called the **foramen magnum.** The **occipital condyles,** located on either side of the foramen magnum, articulate with the top bone of the spinal column. Also, the prominent tubercle on the posterior surface of the occipital bone is called the **external occipital protuberance.** *(See Fig. 11)*

5. The **sphenoid bone** is sometimes described as the "bat-shaped" bone, and helps make up the floor of the cranial cavity, the back of the eye-

sockets, and part of the temple area. One of its prominent landmarks is the **sella turcica,** which is a depression in the center of the superior portion of the sphenoid, and which holds the pituitary gland. In addition, the sphenoid bone also contains **paranasal sinuses.** *(See Fig. 10)*

6. The **ethmoid bone** is a very irregular shaped bone, which helps make up the floor of the cranial cavity, part of the eyesocket, and the upper part of the nasal cavity. It has a number of important landmarks, including the **cribriform plate,** which is the flat, superior surface of the ethmoid, which is involved in making up the floor of the cranial cavity. It contains many small holes for the passage of nerves into the nasal cavity. Also, the ethmoid contains a noticeable vertical projection on its superior portion called the **crista galli.** The crista galli is so named because it is thought to look like a rooster's comb. The **vertical or perpendicular plate** of the ethmoid is a thin, flat plate of bone which extends down into the nasal cavity on the midline, and helps make up the nasal septum. The ethmoid bone also contains **paranasal sinuses.** *(See Fig. 9)*

The **face** is the second main subdivision of the skull, and consists of a total of 14 bones.

1. The **nasal bones** are two small bones making up the area we commonly think of as the bridge of the nose *(See Fig. 8)*

2. The two **lacrimal bones** are located in the anterior, medial portion of the eyesockets. The word lacrimal comes from the Latin word for "tears". *(See Fig. 8)*

3. The **vomer bone** is located on the midline in the base of the nasal cavity. Along with the perpendicular plate of the ethmoid bone, it helps form the nasal septum, which is the wall that divides the nasal cavity into right and left parts. *(See Fig. 8)*

4. The **zygomatic or malar bones** are commonly called the cheek bones. They also help form the eyesocket. *(See Fig. 8)*

5. The **palatine bones** are two small bones which help form the posterior part of the roof of the mouth. It is from these bones which we get the commonly used word "palate", which refers to the roof of the mouth. *(See Fig. 11)*

6. The **maxillary bones** are the upper jaw bones. Although there are technically two maxillary bones, they are often referred to as the **maxilla.** They also help form the eyesocket and the walls of the nasal cavity. The part of the maxilla into which the roots of the teeth are embedded is called the **alveolar process.** The horizontal portion of the maxilla, which forms the anterior portion of the roof of the mouth, is referred to as the palatine process. The maxillary bones actually make up a greater portion of the palate, or bony roof of the mouth, than do the **palatine bones.** Also contained within the maxillary

bones are the two large cavities referred to as the maxillary sinuses. *(See Fig. 9)*

7. The **mandible** is the lower jaw bone. Its main horizontal and anterior portion is referred to as the **body,** while the vertical, posterior portion is called the **ramus.** The inferior, anterior part of the mandible, which we might call the "tip of the chin", is known as the **mental eminence.** Like the maxilla, that portion of the mandible into which the teeth are embedded, the superior part of the body, is referred to as the **alveolar process.** The point at which the inferior line of the body of the mandible turns upward is referred to as the angle of the mandible. The **angle** can be easily felt just inferior to the earlobe. The **mandibular condyle** fits into a depression on the temporal bone, called the **mandibular fossa,** to make up the lower jaw joint. *(See Fig. 8)*

8. Each of the two **inferior nasal concha** can be described as a bony ridge, or "ledge", located on the lateral wall of the nasal cavity. Just above the inferior nasal concha on each side of the nasal cavity are the similar middle and superior conchae. However, these are not separate facial bones, as are the inferior conchae, but are considered part of the ethmoid bone. *(See Fig. 8)*

Besides the cranial and facial bones, the skull contains within it three pairs of tiny ear bones referred to as the **auditory ossicles.** Actually, these little bones are located within the middle ear, which is a small cavity within the temporal bone. These bones are all named for their shapes, and are called the **malleus** (hammer), the **incus** (anvil), and the **stapes** (stirrup). They are important to the hearing process, as they are involved in transmitting vibrations which result when sound waves travel down the hearing canal and strike the ear drum. These vibrations result in impulses which are eventually interpreted as sound by the nerves and specialized structures located in the inner ear.

The **hyoid bone** is a horseshoe shaped bone located in the cervical region, just above the voicebox. It is somewhat unique in that it does not directly articulate with any other bone. It serves as a point of attachment for a number of muscles involved with movements in the tongue, mouth and throat areas. *(See Fig. 12)*

The bones of the spinal column, known as the **vertebrae,** are arranged in a way which allows for both strength and support, plus flexibility and movement. *(See Fig. 13)* Although there are some differences in size, shape, and detail, most of the vertebrae are similar in structure. *(See Fig. 14)* There are 26 of them stacked one on top of another to form the main support structure of the body - the spine. A side view of the spine indicates that it is not a perfectly straight column like you might see supporting the front of a colonial style home, but one with significant curvatures. The spinal column serves not only to support the body, but as a protective passageway for the spinal cord, an essential component of the central nervous system. The 26 vertebrae are usually divided into several main groupings, with the upper seven in the neck area being referred to as **cervical vertebrae**. The most superior of these, or C-1, is also known as the **atlas.** This is the vertebrae which articulates with the occipital bone, and upon which the skull rests. Below the atlas is C-2, or the **axis,** which forms a special articulation with the atlas that allows a pivoting action, enabling the head to be turned from side to side.

The twelve vertebrae inferior to those in the cervical region are designated **thoracic vertebrae**. They could be described as being in the upper back area. They do not have individual names, but are simply designated T-1 through T-12. They do, however, have an important distinction, in that each of them articulates with one of the pairs of ribs. Thus, it makes sense that there would be twelve pairs of ribs to match up with the twelve thoracic vertebrae.

Inferior to the thoracic vertebrae are the five in the lower back area referred to as the **lumbar vertebrae**. They are designated L-1 through L-5.

Immediately inferior to L-5 is the **sacrum,** which is actually a bone resulting from the fusion of five separate vertebrae in a developing child. In addition to the adjacent vertebrae, the sacrum articulates with the two hip bones to help form the pelvis.

The most inferior vertebra, sometimes referred to as the "tail bone", is the **coccyx.** Like the sacrum, the coccyx is a bone which was formed by the fusion of several separate bones in the developmental process.

Besides the skull, hyoid bone, and the spine, the axial skeleton includes the **thorax,** or chest area. The thorax consists of the thoracic vertebrae, the ribs, and the **sternum,** or breastbone. *(See Fig. 15)* The sternum is considered to be a single bone, but was originally three segments during development. The superior segment is called the **manubrium,** the middle segment the **body** or **gladiolus,** and the inferior segment the **xiphoid process**.

There is a total of twelve pairs of ribs, seven of which are attached by their costal cartilages directly to the sternum. These upper seven pairs of ribs are often referred to as **true ribs** as a result of their articulation with the sternum. The bottom five pairs of ribs do not attach directly to the sternum, and are referred to as **false ribs**. Of these, ribs numbered 8, 9, and 10 have cartilages which attach them to the rib above. However, ribs numbered 11 and 12 have no anterior cartilages, and are called **floating ribs.** Posteriorly, each pair of ribs articulates with one of the thoracic vertebrae. *(See Fig. 15)*

Appendicular Skeleton

There are 126 bones in the appendicular skeleton, which consists of the upper and lower extremities, plus the pectoral and pelvic girdles. The pectoral girdle includes the **scapulae,** or shoulder blades, and the **clavicles,** or collar bones. The medial end of the clavicle articulates with the manubrium of the sternum, while the lateral end joins with the superior part of the scapula to help form the shoulder area. The scapula contains several special landmarks, including the **acromion**, which is its superior, lateral projection that articulates

19

with the clavicle, and the **coracoid process**, which serves as an anchoring point for several muscles. The name of the coracoid process is derived from the Latin words meaning "resembling a crow's beak". *(See Figs. 6 & 7)*

The ball-like superior end of the **humerus,** which is known as the **head,** also articulates with the scapula to form the shoulder joint. *(See Fig. 6 & 7)* The word "humerus", which is the scientific name for the upper arm bone, actually means "shoulder" in Latin. The **glenoid cavity** is a depression on the scapula into which the head of the humerus fits in order to form the shoulder joint. The inferior end of the humerus contains smooth, curved articular surfaces called the **humeral condyles**. These condyles articulate with the **radius** and **ulna** to form the elbow joint. As a matter of fact, the word "ulna" comes from the Latin word meaning "elbow". The ulna is the medial of the two forearm bones, and its superior end, which we commonly think of as our elbow, is called the **olecranon process.** The radius is the lateral bone of the forearm, and both it and the ulna articulate with the wrist bones, or **carpals.** There is a total of eight carpal bones in each wrist. *(See Fig. 19)*

The prefix "meta-" comes from the Latin for "beyond", and so the bones of the hand, which are just beyond the wrist bones, are appropriately called **metacarpals.** There are five metacarpals in each hand.

Finally, making up the fingers, are a series of bones called **phalanges,** which comes from the Greek word for "row". Each finger contains a row of three bones, with only two in the thumb. This makes for a total of 14 phalanges in each upper extremity. They are not individually named, but are simply referred to as the proximal, middle, and distal phalange of each finger. Thus, the bones of the ring finger on the left hand, for example, would be called the third proximal, the third middle, and the third distal phalanges of the left hand.

The hip bones, or **os coxa**, make up the so called pelvic girdle. *(See Fig. 16, 17, 18)* Like the sternum, each os coxa originally developed as three separate pieces, which fuse together to become a single bone. The broad, superior portion of the os coxa is called the **ilium,** from the Latin word for "flank". Its upper rim is called the **iliac crest.** The inferior portion, which is the part we would sit on, is called the **ischium,** from the Greek word for "hip". The inferior, anterior segment, just above the genital region, is called the **pubis,** or **pubic bone**. Another important landmark of the os coxa is the **acetabulum,** which is the cup-like area into which the head of the upper leg bone fits to make up the hip joint. Along with the sacrum and coccyx, the two os coxa help make up the **pelvis.** The upper part of the pelvis, basically above the hip joint, is sometimes called the false pelvis, and the inferior portion is called the true pelvis.

The **femur** is the large bone of the upper leg, or the area we might commonly call the thigh. *(See Fig. 6 & 7)* On its superior end, the femoral head articulates with the os coxa in the acetabulum, and the inferior end of the femur consists of two condyles which articulate with a lower leg bone to make up the knee joint. In addition, the inferior, anterior end of the femur articulates with the **patella,** or kneecap. The patella slides up and down in a grove on the femur, and serves as an important point of attachment for several muscles of the leg. It is often categorized as a sesamoid bone, due to the fact that it actually develops within the tendon of one of the femoral muscles. By definition, a sesamoid bone is one which is embedded in tendon.

As mentioned earlier, the inferior end of the femur articulates with the top of the **tibia,** or "shin bone". The tibia is considered the medial bone of the lower leg. Along the anterior margin of the tibia is a rather pronounced ridge, referred to as the **tibial crest**. On the distal end of the tibia is the projection referred to as the **medial malleolus**. Although it is not actually a bone of the ankle, the medial malleolus is what we may commonly refer to as our "inside ankle bone". The projection which we might commonly call our "outside ankle bone" is the **lateral malleolus**. It also is not an ankle bone, but the inferior end of the **fibula,** the lateral bone of the lower leg.

The bones which do make up the ankle area are referred to as **tarsals.** There are seven tarsals in each ankle, one of which is the **calcaneus,** or heel bone. The bones of the foot, or those just beyond the ankle, are referred to as **metatarsals.** There are five of these bones in each foot. And, finally, the bones of the toes are called **phalanges,** just as those in the fingers are. They are equal in number to the phalanges of the fingers, there being a total of 14 phalanges in each foot. Thus, as one can readily see, of the 206 classified bones in the human body, over one quarter, or 56 of them, are phalanges. *(See Fig. 21)*

Arthrology

The prefix "arthro-" refers to joints, or articulations, so the term **arthrology** refers to the study of articulations. An articulation is simply a point of union between two bones, or cartilage and bone, and all bones in the body, except the hyoid bone, articulate with other bones. The joints of the body are often categorized based on the relative amount of movement which exists at the joint. The first of these categories is called a **synarthrosis,** or an immovable articulation. At this type of joint, there is no movement intended by the body. A good example of synarthroses are the **cranial sutures**, which is the name given to the point at which the bones of the cranium come together. The edges of these bones have tightly interlocking teeth-like processes which hold them firmly together. The sternocostal articulations, or the point at which the ribs attach to the sternum, are another example of synarthroses.

Amphiarthroses, or slightly movable articulations, allow a small amount of movement at the joint. Unlike synarthroses, there is often a piece of specialized cartilage separating the two bones in an amphiarthrosis. For example, the **pubic symphysis**, or the point at which the two pubic bones join at the median plane, is classified as an amphiarthrosis. Also, the **sacro-iliac articulation**, where the sacrum meets up with the two os coxae, is another example of a slightly movable articulation. A final example of amphiarthroses are the intervertebral articulations, between the bodies of the vertebrae. Some movement is necessary at these points in order for the body to be able to twist and bend in its normal fashion. Most of the vertebrae are separated by disc-shaped pads of cartilage, which provide needed cushioning between the bones.

The third major category of articulations are the **diarthroses,** or freely movable articulations. These types of joints allow significant movement - sometimes only in one direction, and sometimes in several directions. As opposed to other joints, diarthroses are characterized by the fact that they posses a sleeve, or capsule, which surrounds the joint. Within this capsule is the joint cavity, which is lined with a smooth, connective tissue membrane called synovial membrane. This membrane secretes a lubricating fluid to reduce friction in the joint. Also present in these types of joints are layers of articular cartilage which cover the ends of the bones forming the joints. Diarthroses are the most numerous of the articulations in the body. Examples of freely movable articulations are those in the hip, knee, elbow, and shoulder areas.

Ligaments are tough bands of fibrous connective tissue which help to stabilize a diarthritic joint. They actually help hold the two bones together in their proper position, and restrict movement from occurring in the wrong direction. However, sudden and excessive force applied to a joint can cause a tearing of these ligaments. Torn knee ligaments are a common athletic type of injury, especially when strong force is applied to the knee area from the side, or when the knee twists abnormally while bearing weight.

Closely associated with most freely movable joints, but also found in other areas of the body, are small, fluid-filled sacs called **bursae.** Bursae provide additional cushioning and friction reducing properties to areas of the body where a lot of movement occurs. They are usually found in such areas as where tendons rub over bones, between ligaments and bones, or between muscles and bones.

THE MUSCULAR SYSTEM
Chapter 4

The prefix "myo-" comes from the Latin word meaning muscle, so the term **myology** refers to the study of the muscular system. *(See Fig. 22 & 23)* Muscles make up approximately 45% of body weight, and are responsible for imparting movement to body parts. The reason that muscles can create bodily movements is that they possess the unique ability to contract, or shorten in length. This ability to contract and cause movement is often referred to as **contractility.** Muscle cells have the ability to convert chemical energy derived from digested food products into mechanical energy, which in turn creates the contractions and movement associated with muscles. A muscle which is fully contracted may be only 1/3 to 1/2 of its normal length when at rest. Muscular movements vary tremendously in the human body, from the blink of an eyelid, to the chewing of food, to contraction of the urinary bladder while expelling urine, to the complex acts of walking or throwing a ball. Nevertheless, each of these movements involve the principle of contractility.

However, muscles do not simply contract on their own, but must receive a stimulus from the nervous system in order to do so. Specialized nerve cells, or neurons, which transmit stimuli to muscle cells are called motor neurons. The combination of a motor neuron and the group of muscle cells which it stimulates is called a **motor unit.**

Generally, muscles do not act individually to create movement of a body part, but function in coordination with other muscles. However, there is often one muscle which is largely responsible for a desired action, and it may be referred to as the agonist, or **prime mover.** For example, when flexing the elbow joint, the biceps brachii muscle in the front of the upper arm would be the prime mover. At the same time, the triceps brachii muscle in the back of the upper arm is relaxing, and may be referred to as the antagonist. When the elbow joint is straightened out, the triceps muscle contracts, creating the movement, and it would now be referred to as the prime mover. At the same time, the biceps would be relaxed, so it is now the **antagonist.** Therefore, we can say that the antagonist muscle has the opposite effect of the prime mover.

In addition to the important function of creating movement, muscles also enable the body to maintain its posture. Partial muscular contraction, called **tonic contraction,** does not create movement, but simply allows for a relatively constant amount of tension in a muscle so that it can hold a body part in its proper position. Without this proper muscle tone, the human body would be unable to maintain its upright posture, and would collapse on the ground in a heap!

Besides creating movement and maintaining posture, muscles are responsible for heat production in the body. When muscles contract, energy is expended, and heat is generated, and this helps in maintaining the normal body temperature.

Types of Muscle Tissue

There are three basic categories of muscle tissue: **skeletal** muscle, **smooth** muscle, and cardiac muscle. Skeletal muscle makes up the greatest share of the muscular tissue in the human body, and it is this main type of tissue which we will concentrate our studies upon. Skeletal muscle is so called because it attaches to the bones of the skeleton, and by contracting when necessary, creates movement by pulling on these bones. Skeletal muscle is also known as **voluntary** muscle, because it can be made to contract by conscious or voluntary control. A third name for skeletal muscle is **striated** muscle, because under a microscope, this type of muscle is seen to contain dark colored stripes or striations.

The second main type of muscle tissue in the body is called **smooth,** or **non-striated** muscle. This is because microscopically the muscle tissue does not contain the striations associated with skeletal muscle. Smooth muscle may also be called **involuntary** muscle, because it is found in various organs which work "automatically", and not under our conscious control, such as our internal viscera. Because this type of muscle is found in most of the viscera, it is also referred to as **visceral** muscle. An example of visceral muscle would be that found in the walls of the stomach and intestines, which helps to churn up the food which is being digested, and move it along the digestive tract.

Cardiac muscle is the third main category of muscle tissue, and as its name implies, is found in the heart. Cardiac muscle is unique in that it has some of the characteristics of each of the preceding two groups of muscle tissue. That is, it does have striations when viewed microscopically, but it is also involuntary. Individual cardiac muscle cells are arranged and interconnected somewhat differently than other muscle cells. This functional arrangement helps these cells of the heart muscle to contract as a unit, and to keep doing so in a constant, rhythmic fashion, so that our normal heartbeat can be maintained.

Structure of Skeletal Muscle

As we have already discussed, one of the main functions of muscle tissue is to create movement, and skeletal muscles do this by pulling on the bones to which they are attached. In actuality, muscle tissue is not attached directly to a bone, but is attached to the periosteum, or outer layer of a bone, by strong, dense cords of connective tissue called tendons. Tendons are responsible for attaching muscles to bone (or muscles to muscles in some cases), and they often cross over an articulation in order to pull on the bones forming the joint thus bringing them toward each other.

Let's think of voluntary muscles as having three main parts: an origin, an insertion, and a body. When a muscle contracts, and pulls two articulating bones toward one another, the two bones do not usually move an equal amount. Generally speaking, the end of the muscle which is attached to the less movable, or "fixed", bone is called the **origin,** and the end of the muscle which is attached to the more movable bone is called the **insertion.** The main, fleshy portion of the muscle is called the **body** or **belly** of the muscle. In addition, when describing bones of the extremities, the origin of a muscle is normally the **proximal** end, and the insertion is the **distal** end of the muscle. For example, consider the biceps brachii muscle in the front of the upper arm which helps to bend the elbow joint. While the body of the muscle is evident in the upper arm area, the tendons at its origin cross over the shoulder joint and attach to the scapula, while the tendons at its insertion cross over the elbow joint to attach to the radius bone in the forearm. When the muscle contracts, movement in the vicinity of its origin (shoulder) is minimal, while movement at its insertion (elbow area) is much greater.

Microscopically, muscles consist of many long, cylindrical cells called **muscle fibers.** Each muscle fiber is made up of tiny, thread-like structures called myofibrils, which in turn consist of even finer filaments made up of specialized proteins. The manner in which these filaments are arranged within a muscle fiber produce the characteristic striations mentioned earlier.

Forms of Muscle Contraction

In addition to **tonic** contraction mentioned earlier, there are several other types of muscular contraction, including **twitch** contractions, **tetanic** contractions, **isotonic** contractions, and **isometric** contractions. Twitch contractions are rapid, jerky contractions in response to a stimulus, which play no major role in normal bodily activities, but are often seen research settings.

Tetanic contractions are more sustained contractions, where muscle fibers are unable to relax between stimuli occurring at a more rapid rate. The resulting "tetanus", or state of contraction, may vary in intensity, and is not necessarily an efficient, maximized contraction of all of the fibers in a particular muscle. For example, the name of the disease tetanus is associated with the concept of tetanic contraction, where many of the muscles in the body are stimulated into sustained contractions as a result of bacterial toxins which are put forth by the organism causing the disease. In addition, tetanic contractions may be associated with hypofunction of the parathyroid glands, which are involved in helping regulate the body's use of calcium, an important element affecting normal muscular contractions. Cramps and convulsions are other examples of involuntary tetanic contractions which may affect the body.

Isotonic contractions are those which we normally think of when muscles undergo their normal movement, where a more constant, equal contraction is involved. When an isotonic contraction occurs, the muscle shortens and pulls on another body part, such as a bone, in order to create movement.

Isometric contractions involve a constant tension put upon a muscle, but little or no movement occurs. Although tension increases within the muscle, the muscle does not shorten and result in movement of a body part. This may be demonstrated by pressing your palm down on a desk top while sitting, or holding a heavy book out to the side with your arm extended. Both isotonic and isometric exercises are important and popular methods of improving muscle strength.

Naming of Skeletal Muscles

Although there are literally hundreds of individual skeletal muscles, most of them have names which reflect something important about the muscle, such as its location or action. There are a number of criteria which are most often used to name skeletal muscles in the human body. One of these criteria is **shape**. A number of muscles are named according to their shape, such as the deltoid muscle in the shoulder area. The word "deltoid" is one which combines the word "delta", from the Greek for triangle, and the suffix "-oid", meaning resembling. So the deltoid is a triangular shaped muscle of the shoulder, and it has to do with lifting the arm out to the side. Another example of a muscle named for its shape is the small pyramidalis muscle in the lower abdomen, which is named for its pyramid shape.

Another criterion used is that of **location**. Many muscles are identified based on their general location, such as those containing the word "dorsi" for back, "abdominis" for the abdominal region, or "femoris" for the femoral area. In addition, the muscle may be named based on whether it's located toward or away from the median plane of the body, such as the vastus medialis or the vastus lateralis muscles of the femoral region.

The **direction of the muscle fibers** is also employed in naming muscles. The direction of these muscle fibers is usually described in reference to the midline of the body, or to the long axis of one of the bones in the extremities. For example, the rectus (L.=straight) abdominis muscle runs straight down the front of the abdomen, while the rectus femoris muscle runs straight down the front of the upper leg. Also, the oblique muscles of the abdomen are so named because they run obliquely, or at an angle, to the midline of the body.

The relative **size** of a muscle is another important reason for naming muscles. The terms maximus, major, or magnus, may be used to describe a large muscle, while a small muscle may have the word minimus, or minor, in its name. Another example would be using the words longus (long) and brevis (brief, or short) to describe muscle size.

Muscles are also named based on the **number of divisions** or parts which make up the muscle, such as the word biceps, which literally means two heads (bi meaning two, and ceps, from cephalic, meaning head). Likewise, the triceps would have three divisions, and the quadriceps four divisions. Closely related to these muscular divisions is the fact that many muscles get their names based on the **points of attachment** of the different parts of the muscle. For example, the sternocleidomastoideus muscle is so named because it is attached at its origin to the sternum and the clavicle, and is inserted on the mastoid process of the temporal bone, just behind the earlobe.

Another factor involved is whether the muscle is relatively **superficial** or **deep.** The internal oblique muscles, by definition, would be deeper, or more internal, than the external obliques, which would be more superficial.

Finally, one of the most important reasons for naming skeletal muscles is the **action** they impart to various body parts. As we discussed earlier, creating movement is the main function of muscles, and many of these movements, or actions, are individually described as follows:

1. **Abduction** - moving a body part, such as a limb, away from the median plane of the body. Lifting your arm out to the side is abduction, and the muscles which accomplish this action are called abductors.

2. **Adduction** - moving a body part toward the median plane. Bringing your arm back down to your side would be adduction, and the muscles responsible would be called adductors.

3. **Flexion** - this action may be described as bending a body part, or decreasing the angle between two bones, as in bending the elbow joint, which in turn would decrease the angle between the humerus and the forearm bones. The muscles involved would be called flexors.

4. **Extension** - straightening out a body part, or increasing the angle between bones. Straightening out the elbow joint which was just flexed would be extension, and the muscles doing it are called extensors.

5. **Pronation** - movement of the palm of the hand from a forward or upward facing position to a backward or downward facing position. In pronation, the distal end of the radius crosses over the ulna. Muscles performing pronation are called pronators.

6. **Supination** - movement of the palm of the hand from a backward or downward facing position to a forward or upward position. In supination, the radius and ulna are parallel. The muscles are called supinators.

7. **Elevation** - lifting up a body part. Muscles which do this are called elevators, or just levators.

8. **Depression** - downward movement, or lowering, of a body part. Muscles which do this are called depressors.

9. **Rotation** - movement of a bone around its longitudinal axis. You can rotate your leg medially by pointing your toes inward, or rotate it laterally by pointing your toes outward. Also, the atlas bone rotates on the axis when you turn your head from side to side.

10. **Circumduction** - turning, or swinging, a body part, such as a limb, in a circular fashion. This movement is actually a combination of other actions mentioned above.

11. **Constriction and dilation** - constriction refers to the squeezing closed of a body orifice, and dilation refers to the widening or opening of the orifice. These terms usually refer to the actions of rings of muscle tissue called sphincters, which act as valves to guard body openings.

12. **Protraction and retraction** - protraction refers to the forward movement of a body part, and retraction to the backward movement of a part.

13. **Eversion and Inversion** - the term eversion is used to describe an outward turning of the sole of the foot, and inversion means an inward turning of the sole of the foot.

As we will see when we examine the names of additional muscles in the body, many of them are named based on a combination of these criteria. For example, the flexor carpi radialis muscle is named for what it does (flexing the wrist) and where it is located (radial side of the forearm), and the external obliques are named for the fact that they are relatively superficial (external), and the direction of the muscle fibers (oblique).

Main Muscle Groups

Head and Neck Muscles

Probably the most significant muscles of the head are those which are often described as muscles of facial expression.*(See Fig. 24)* In many instances they differ from other skeletal muscles because they insert into the skin, or other muscles, instead of a bone. This allows for a greater variety of movements, and consequently a wide number of facial expressions and emotions are possible. For example, the **zygomaticus major** muscle draws the corners of the mouth outward and upward, and has often been referred to as the "smiling muscle". The **orbicularis oris** muscle is involved in puckering the lips, and is sometimes called the "kissing muscle". The **buccinator muscle**, in the cheek area, helps puff the cheeks out, and has consequently been called the "trumpeters" muscle. Other examples include the **frontalis muscle**, which helps raise the eyebrows, the **risorius**, which draws the corners of the mouth laterally as in tension, or "false smiling", and the **platysma**, which pulls the lower lip down and back, as in a look of horror.

Another important group of muscles are the **muscles of mastication**, which have to do with the chewing and grinding of food. This group of muscles includes the **temporalis**, the **masseter**, the **internal** (medial) **pterygoid**, and the **external** (lateral) **pterygoid**. As you might guess, the temporalis is so named because it is attached to the temporal bone. The word "masseter" comes from the Greek for "chewer".*(See Fig. 24)* The pterygoid muscles are also named for one of their attachments, which is the pterygoid, or wing-shaped, portion of the sphenoid bone.

The top of the head is covered by a combination of two muscles, the frontalis muscle in the forehead area and the occipitalis muscle in the back of the head, plus a tendinous sheet of tissue over the top of the cranium called the **galea aponeurotica**.*(See Fig. 22)* The term **aponeurosis** is used to refer to any broad, flat tendon in the body. This entire structure is often referred to as the **occipitofrontalis**, or **epicranius**.

In addition to the platysma muscle mentioned earlier, another important muscle of the neck area is the **sternocleidomastoideus.**(See Fig. 22 & 25) This large muscle is important for its action of moving the head, but also is noted for the fact that the distance between the lateral margins of the two muscles marks the widest part of the neck. The sternocleidomastoideus also serves as the anatomical guide for locating the major blood vessels in the neck, which lie just behind its medial border.

Located in the front of the neck area is a region referred to as the **anterior cervical** triangle. This region is noted because it outlines the vicinity in which the common carotid artery and the internal jugular vein are located. The boundaries of the anterior cervical triangle are as follows:(See Fig. 25)

1) The midline of the neck - medial boundary

2) The inferior margin of the mandible - superior boundary

3) The anterior border of the sternocleidomastoideus - lateral boundary

As you can imagine, these muscles of the face and neck area are extremely important for the various actions and expressions they impart, but are also important for providing surface shape and form to the body.

Trunk Muscles

The **pectoralis major** is an important muscle located in the anterior chest area, and is involved with moving the upper arm.(See Fig. 22) It is appropriately named, as the word "pectoral" comes from the Latin word for breast. Also in the thoracic area are the intercostal muscles, meaning "between the ribs". These include both the **internal** and **external intercostals**, and they are important for their involvement in the expansion and contraction of the thoracic area which occurs during breathing.(See Fig. 22) Along with the intercostals, the **phrenic muscle**, or **diaphragm,** is extremely important in the breathing process. The diaphragm is often described as a dome-shaped sheet of muscle which forms the floor of the thoracic cavity, or conversely, the roof of the abdominal cavity. During breathing, the diaphragm flattens out and enlarges the size of the thoracic cavity, which helps to draw air into the lungs. The diaphragm contains several main openings to allow the passage of major structures between the thoracic and abdominal cavities. These main openings include the esophageal orifice for the esophagus, the vena caval orifice for the inferior vena cava, and the aortic orifice for passage of the aorta. When the aorta passes through the diaphragm its designation changes from thoracic to abdominal aorta. In addition to these openings, the center of the diaphragm is composed of a sheet of tendon referred to as the **central tendon.**

The muscles of the abdomen are often categorized by their general location, such as anteromedial, anterolateral, and posterior abdomen. These muscles tend to be arranged in several layers, with the muscle fibers of each layer running at different angles.(See Fig. 22) This makes for a strong, supportive structure to enclose and protect the abdominal organs. The **rectus abdominus** muscle is one of the anteromedial abdomen muscles, and runs from the sternum and rib cage straight down to the pubic bone. The **external and internal oblique** muscles run at angles down the anterior lateral part of the abdomen, with the transversus muscles underneath them. An important posterior abdominal muscle is the **psoas major**, which runs from the lumbar vertebrae down to the femur. Not only is it involved in moving the femur, but along the medial border of the psoas major muscle runs the external iliac artery and vein, so the muscle serves as an anatomical guide in locating these important vessels.

Two significant muscles of the back are the trapezius, which comes from the Latin for "trapezoid shaped", and the latissimus dorsi, from the Latin words for "wide" and "back". The **trapezius** is in the upper back, and actually runs from the back of the occipital bone, down to the thoracic vertebrae, and over to the acromion (the superior lateral projection) of the scapula. The **latissimus dorsi** is a large, lower back muscle, which is attached to the humerus and is involved in its movement. *(See Fig. 23)*

The **erector spinae** is another group of muscles in the back, which run vertically from the lower back area up to the more superior vertebrae and ribs. As the name implies, these muscles are primarily involved with movement of the vertebral column, and help keep the spine in an erect position.

Upper Extremity and Shoulder Muscles

The **deltoid** is a large, triangular shaped muscle making up most of the mass of the shoulder area. *(See Fig. 23)* It is involved mainly in abduction of the humerus. Also, the teres major muscle, which runs from the scapula to the upper part of the humerus, is involved in movements of the upper arm. It is also noted for the fact that it serves as the point at which the axillary artery terminates and becomes known as the brachial artery.

In the upper arm area, the **coracobrachialis** muscle is an example of one which is named for its points of attachment - the coracoid (Greek=raven, or crow's beak) process of the scapula and the upper part of the arm, or brachium. *(See Fig. 22)* Besides its actions in moving the arm, the coracobrachialis serves as the anatomical guide for the axillary artery, which is located just behind its medial border.

The upper arm also contains several muscles which are involved in flexing and extending the elbow joint. *(See Fig. 22 & 23)* The flexors on the anterior surface include the **brachialis** and the **biceps brachii**, and on the back of the humerus is the **triceps brachii**, which extends the elbow joint.

There are a number of muscles in the forearm area which have to do with movements of the forearm bones, the wrist, and the fingers. *(See Fig. 22)* The **brachioradialis** is a muscle located in the superior lateral part of the forearm, which assists the brachialis and biceps brachii muscles in flexing the forearm. Other important examples include the supinator and pronator muscles, which, as their names imply, have to do with supination and pronation of the hand. The **flexor carpi radialis** and the **flexor carpi ulnaris** muscles are also appropriately named, as they act to flex the wrist. In addition to this action, the tendons of these muscles, in the wrist area, serve as important anatomical guides in locating the radial and ulnar arteries, which lie just lateral to the respective tendons. Another forearm muscle, the **flexor digitorum superficialis**, has to do with flexing the digits, or fingers.

Lower Extremity Muscles

The **gluteus** (Greek=buttock) **maximus** muscle makes up the bulk of the buttocks area, and is important for its action of extending the thigh. *(See Fig. 23)* In the anterior femoral region, there is a group of four muscles called the **quadriceps,** which includes the rectus femoris and the three vastus muscles. *(See Fig. 22)* These muscles serve to extend the lower leg at the knee joint. Also on the anterior surface of the thigh is the **sartorius** (L.=tailor) muscle, which is a superficial, strap-like muscle running obliquely across the thigh to the inner side of the knee area. The sartorius is important for its involvement as the lateral boundary of the femoral triangle. The femoral triangle is a region on the superior anterior surface of the thigh, which serves as an important anatomical guide in locating the femoral vessels, which run through the center of this triangular area. *(See Fig. 26)* The boundaries of the femoral triangle are as follows:

1) Superior - inguinal ligament

2) Medial - adductor longus muscle

3) Lateral – sartorius muscle

The medial side of the thigh is occupied by a group of muscles called the **adductors,** which are involved in adduction of the leg, or returning it toward the median plane. *(See Fig. 22 & 23)* Among others, this group includes the **adductor longus** and the **adductor magnus** muscles. As previously mentioned, the adductor longus is the medial boundary of the femoral triangle, and the adductor magnus contains a canal-like opening, called the adductor canal (Hunter's canal), through which the femoral vessels and nerves pass. This opening also serves as the point at which the femoral artery terminates and becomes known as the popliteal.

The posterior aspect of the thigh contains a group of muscles commonly called the **"hamstring".** *(See Fig. 23)* These muscles, which flex the lower leg, include the **biceps femoris**, the **semitendinous**, and the **semimembranous**. At the base of the popliteal space, running at an angle from the bottom of the femur to the top of the tibia is the **popliteus** muscle. The inferior border of this muscle marks the point at which the popliteal artery terminates by bifurcating into the anterior and posterior tibial arteries.

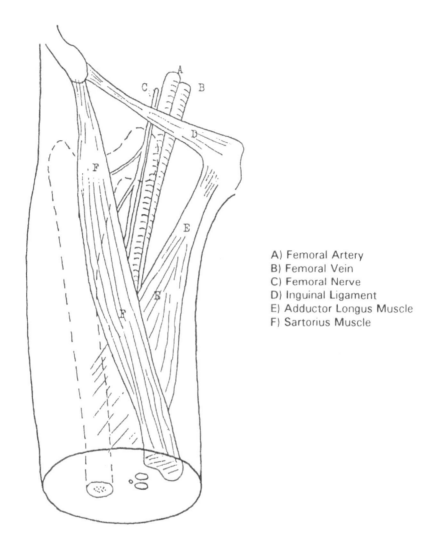

A) Femoral Artery
B) Femoral Vein
C) Femoral Nerve
D) Inguinal Ligament
E) Adductor Longus Muscle
F) Sartorius Muscle

Femoral Triangle and Position of Vessels
(Right lower extremity viewed from the anterior aspect)

Several other muscles of the lower leg include the **tibialis anterior** in the front of the leg, and the **gastrocnemius** (Gr.=belly of the leg) and **soleus** (L.=flat) muscles in the posterior lower leg, or calf area. Both the gastrocnemius and soleus are attached to the heel bone (calcaneus) by the strong calcaneal tendon, commonly called the **Achilles tendon**. These two muscles have to do with extending the foot, thus allowing you to "stand on your toes". *(See Fig. 22 & 23)*

The tables on the following pages provide a quick reference to the main muscles of the body according to their general location:

TABLE D
Muscles of the Head and Neck

Muscle	Origin	Insertion	Action
Frontalis	galea aponeuroitca	eyebrows and root	raises eyebrows of nose area
Occipitalis	occipital bone	galea aponeurotica	draws scalp back
Orbicularis oculi	encircles eye	encircles eye	closes eye
Orbicularis oris	encircles lips	encircles lips	closes lips
Zygomaticus	zygomatic bone	skin/muscle at corner of mouth	draws upper lip back and up
Levator An guli oris	maxilla	skin/muscle at corner of mouth	raises angle of the mouth
Depressor anguli oris	mandible	skin/muscle at corner of mouth	draws angle of mouth down
Risorius	masseter muscle	angle of the mouth	draws angle of backward
Levator palpebra superioris	sphenoid bone	eyelid	raises upper eyelid
Buccinator	maxilla and mandible	orbicularis oris	compresses cheek
Corrugator	frontal bone	skin of eyebrow	draws eyebrows down and in
Procerus	bridge of nose	skin above nose	draws skin of forehead down
Levator labii superioris	maxilla	upper lip	raises upper lip
Depressor labii inferioris	mandible	lower lip	draws lower lip down
Mentalis	mandible	skin of chin	protrudes lower lip
Temporalis	temporal bone	mandible	closes jaw
Masseter	zygomatic arch	mandible	closes jaw
Medial pterygoid	sphenoid, palatine, & maxilla	mandible	helps in mastication
Lateral pterygoid	sphenoid	mandible	helps in mastication
Sternocleidomastoid	sternum and clavicle	mastoid process of temporal bone	rotates and flexes head
Platysma	clavicle and pectoralis muscle	mandible	depresses mandible & lip
Digastricus	mandible	hyoid bone	elevates hyoid
Omohyoid	scapula	hyoid bone	depresses hyoid

TABLE E
Muscles of the Thorax

Muscle	Origin	Insertion	Action
Pectoralis major	sternum, clavicle,	humerus	flexes and adducts arm
External intercostals	ribs	ribs	elevate ribs in breathing
Internal intercostals	ribs	ribs	depress ribs in breathing
Diaphragm	sternum, ribs, & vertebrae	central tendon	increases chest capacity for breathing

TABLE F
Muscles of the Back

Muscle	Origin	Insertion	Action
Trapezius	occipital. bone / upper vertibrae	clavicle and scapula	extends head, raises scapula
Latissimus dorsi	lower vertebrae & ilium	humerus	extends and adducts arm

Table G
Muscles of the Abdomen

Muscle	Origin	Insertion	Action
Rectus Abdominus	pubis	5th-7th ribs	flexes trunk
External obliques	ribs	midline of the abdomen	compresses the abdomen
Internal obliques	iliac crest, linguinal ligament	midline of the abdomen	compresses the abdomen
Transversus	ribs, vertebrae,	midline of the abdomen	compresses the abdomen
Psoas major	lumbar vertebrae	medial femur	flexes thigh

Table H
Muscles of the Shoulder

Muscle	Origin	Insertion	Action
Deltoid	clavicle and scapula	humerus	abducts arm
Teres major	scapula	humerus	rotates and adducts arm

Table I
Muscles of the Arm

Muscle	Origin	Insertion	Action
Biceps brachii	scapula	radius	flexes lower arm at elbow
Brachialis	humerus	ulna	flexes lower arm at elbow
Triceps brachii	scapula & humerus	ulna	extends lower arm

Table J
Muscles of the Lower Extremity

Muscle	Origin	Insertion	Action
Gluteus maximus	ilium, sacrum, coccyx	femur	extends thigh
Adductor longus	pubis	femur	adducts thigh
Adductor magnus	ischium & pubis	femur	adducts thigh
Sartorius	iliac spine	superior, medial tibia	flexes and rotates leg
Rectus femoris	ilium	tibia	extends lower leg
Vastus latteralis, medialis, & intermedius	femur	tibia	extends lower leg
Biceps femoris	ischium & femur	fibula	flexes lower leg
Semitendinous	ischium	\tibia	flexes lower leg
Semimembranous	ischium	tibia	flexes lower leg
Popliteus	femur	tibia	rotates lower leg
Tibialis anterior	upper tibia	ankle area	flexes foot
Gastrocnemius	femur	calcaneus	extends foot
Soleus	tibia / fibula	calcaneus	extends foot

THE DIGESTIVE SYSTEM

Chapter 5

As we all know, food and water are essential to life. The digestive system in the human body provides us with these necessary products, which will be broken down by the organs of the digestive system for eventual use by the individual cells of the body. Because most of the food molecules we take in are too large to pass through the walls of the digestive tract and be used by the body, they must be reduced to simpler structures both mechanically and chemically. This process of breaking down ingested food into simpler products suitable for absorption, then metabolism by the body, is defined as **digestion**.

Mechanical digestion involves the physical pulverization of food by chewing to break it into smaller bits, then swallowing it and having the smooth muscles in the walls of the digestive tract churn the food up so that it will be satisfactorily mixed with the chemical enzymes present in the tract. Chemical digestion has to do with enzymes splitting large molecules into smaller ones capable of being absorbed through the walls of the digestive tract and into the blood or lymph vessels. For example, carbohydrates are broken down into simpler sugars, fats into glycerol and fatty acids, and proteins into amino acids. These are the products of digestion which are small enough to be absorbed and eventually consumed by the cells of the body undergoing everyday metabolism.

The organs of the digestive system are often broken down into two main groups: the **alimentary canal,** or **gastro-intestinal** tract, and the accessory organs of digestion. The alimentary (L.=nutrition) canal is a muscular tube extending through the entire body, from the mouth to the anal canal. It is approximately 29-30 feet long, and includes the mouth, pharynx, esophagus, stomach, small and large intestines, and the anus. The accessory organs of digestion include the teeth, tongue, salivary glands, liver, gallbladder, and pancreas.

The general structure of the walls of the digestive tract involves four main layers, identified as follows:

1. **mucosa** - the inner lining of mucous membrane *(See Fig. 30)*

2. **submucosa** - the connective tissue layer underneath the mucous membrane, which contains many blood vessels, lymph tissue, and nerve endings *(See Fig. 30)*

3. **muscularis** - two layers of smooth muscle tissue, one arranged in circular rings around the tube, and the other in longitudinal fashion. Contractions of these muscle layers, called **peristalsis,** is what helps propel the contents of the digestive tract along *(See Fig. 30)*

4. **serosa** - the outer layer of serous membrane. In the abdominal area this membrane is also known as visceral peritoneum. One particular section of peritoneum which anchors the intestines to the posterior abdominal wall, and transmits vessels and nerves, is known as the **mesentery.***(See Fig. 30)*

Mouth

The mouth is also known as the **oral** or **buccal** cavity. *(See Fig. 27)* That portion of the mouth between the teeth and the lips and cheeks is known as the **vestibule.** The bony roof of the mouth, made up of the palatine part of the maxilla plus the palatines bones, is called the **hard palate**. Posterior to the hard palate is the **soft palate**, an area of fibrous and muscular tissue, behind which the nasal cavity communicates with the upper part of the throat. Projecting down from the soft palate is a small, finger-like projection called the **uvula.**

The **tongue** is a highly mobile, muscular organ which occupies the floor of the oral cavity. *(See Fig. 27)* It is an important organ in voice production, and aids in the process of mastication, or chewing. In addition, the tongue contains taste buds, which are highly specialized nerve endings that allow us to experience the four basic qualities of taste: sweet, sour, salty, and bitter.

Tonsils are masses of lymphoid tissue located in the posterior, lateral part of the mouth (palatine tonsils), on the tongue (lingual tonsils), and on the upper part of the throat (pharyngeal tonsils, or adenoids). Most of us have experienced tonsils which become swollen and tender during infections of the throat area. The tonsils are swollen because they are performing their normal duty of filtering bacteria. However, tonsils often become chronically swollen and can affect the passage of air into the respiratory system, and doctors may decide to remove them surgically in an operation called a tonsillectomy.

There are three pairs of **salivary glands** which deliver saliva to the oral cavity to aid in the digestive process. Saliva is continuously secreted to help keep the mucous membranes lining the mouth in a moist condition, but its secretion is increased when food enters the mouth. Saliva contains an enzyme called salivary amylase which begins the digestion of carbohydrates. The salivary glands are identified as follows based on their location:

1. **parotid** glands (para=in the vicinity of + oto=ear) - located in the posterior lower jaw area, just in front of the lower part of the ear

2. **sublingual** glands (sub=under + lingual=tongue) - located in the floor of the oral cavity, under the tongue

3. **submandibular** glands - located behind and beneath the body of the mandible, slightly posterior to the sublingual glands

Teeth are specialized organs for the biting, tearing, and chewing of food, and are situated in sockets within the alveolar processes of the maxilla and the mandible. *(See Fig. 27)* A typical tooth has three main parts: the crown, which is the visible portion above the surface; the neck, which is the part behind the gums; and the root, which is an elongated section fitting down into the socket in the bone. The crown of the tooth is covered with an extremely hard substance called **enamel,** which is well suited to the rigors of chewing and grinding food over the years.

The first set of teeth which develops in a child, generally between about six months and two years of age, are called **deciduous,** or **milk** teeth. They consist of a total of twenty teeth, identified as incisors, canines, and molars. The **incisors** are the front teeth (4 top and 4 bottom) which have sharp edges adapted for cutting into food. Next to the incisors are the **canine** teeth (2 top and 2 bottom), which are more pointed, and are suited for tearing of food, particularly in animals such as dogs, from which we get the name of this set of teeth. The back teeth, or **molars** (4 top and 4 bottom), have flatter surfaces for the grinding of food products.

A child generally begins to shed the deciduous teeth by about age six, and by about age twelve, all of these baby teeth have been replaced by permanent ones. Adult incisors replace deciduous incisors, canines replace canines, and adult pre-molars, or bicuspids, replace the child's molars. In addition, twelve more molars generally appear over the next ten to twelve years, so by the time an adult is twenty-two to twenty-four years old, they have a total of thirty-two permanent teeth. The last, back set of molars to appear is often referred to as "wisdom teeth". These teeth often fail to grow and emerge in a proper fashion, and may need to be extracted in order that the other teeth have adequate room to develop.

The Pharynx and Esophagus

The **pharynx,** or throat, is sometimes described as a "funnel-shaped" organ, which is situated on the anterior surface of the cervical vertebrae. The pharynx is usually divided into three anatomical divisions. *(See Fig. 39)* The upper portion, which communicates with the nasal passages, is called the **nasopharynx.** Also located in the nasopharynx are two openings into the auditory, or **eustachian tubes.** These tubes are passageways which connect the middle ear to the throat, and allow for the equalization of pressure between the middle ear and the outside of the body. The middle section, behind the mouth, is referred to as the **oropharynx.** The inferior segment is the **laryngopharynx,** which is so named because it communicates with the larynx, or voice box, of the respiratory system. Certainly both air and food must pass through the throat, so the pharynx is considered a dual organ, common to both the respiratory and digestive systems. The pharynx not only serves as a passageway for air between the nasal cavity and the larynx, but as a passageway for food between the mouth and the esophagus.

The **esophagus** is a muscular tube, approximately ten inches long, which serves as a passageway for food between the pharynx and the stomach. *(See Fig. 28)* As was mentioned in the chapter on muscles, one of the main openings in the diaphragm, through which the esophagus passes in order to reach the stomach, is called the esophageal orifice. The esophagus has no digestive or absorptive functions, but merely a delivery one. When swallowing occurs, waves of muscular contractions, called **peristalsis,** help to move the food through the esophagus and into the stomach.

The Stomach

The **stomach** may be described as a "pouch-like" dilation of the alimentary canal, which serves as a reservoir for food to be further mixed with digestive juices prior to entering the small intestine. *(See Fig. 28)* The walls of the stomach contain smooth muscles which assist digestion by mechanically churning and mixing the food which has entered from the esophagus. In addition, gastric glands in the walls of the stomach secrete hydrochloric acid and other enzymes, such as pepsin, which further the chemical digestion of foods, particularly proteins. By the time food is ready to leave the stomach, it has been converted into a creamy, semi-solid substance called **chyme.** The mucous membrane lining the stomach helps to keep the digestive enzymes from digesting the walls of the stomach along with the food.

Two sphincter valves guard the entrance and the exit from the stomach. The valve around the entrance to the stomach, where the esophagus empties in, is called the **cardiac sphincter valve**, and the general vicinity around this opening is called the **cardia,** or cardiac region. The valve at the exit from the stomach is referred to as the **pyloric sphincter valve**, and the lower right portion of the stomach, just before this exit, is called the **pylorus.** The upper left portion of the stomach, which has a curved, dome-shaped appearance, is known as the **fundus.** The term body is given to the main, central part of the stomach. There are also two main curvatures identified on the stomach. The upper right, or medial margin of the stomach is called the **lesser curvature,** and the lower left, or lateral one, is known as the **greater curvature**. *(See Fig. 28)*

The Small Intestine

After food passes through the pyloric sphincter valve, it enters into the small intestine. It is called the "small" intestine because its diameter is significantly less than that of the large intestine, but it is certainly not small in length, as it measures approximately twenty feet long. The first and shortest segment (10-12") is called the **duodenum.** *(See Fig. 28)* The second, or middle section, is the **jejunum,** and the third portion of the small intestine is known as the **ileum.** The ileum terminates in the lower right abdominal area by emptying its contents into the first part of the large intestine. *(See Fig. 31)* The point at which the ileum empties into the large intestine is guarded by another sphincter valve called the **ileo-cecal** valve.

The small intestine is the main organ in the digestive tract where the absorption of nutrients takes place. Additional digestive juices are added in the duodenum, including bile from the liver, pancreatic juice from the pancreas, and other digestive enzymes from glands in the submucosa called **Brunner's glands**. By the time these food products reach the latter portions of the small intestine, they have been broken down to the point where nutrients can be absorbed into the underlying blood and lymph vessels. A view of a cross section of the intestinal wall indicates that it is not smooth, but contains millions of tiny, hair-like projections called **villi,** which greatly increase the absorbing surface of the small intestine. *(See Fig. 28)* Also occupying the walls of the small intestine, particularly the ileum, are many small masses of lymphoid tissue, called **Peyer's patches**, which help to keep bacteria present in the food residue from entering the blood stream.

The Liver, Gallbladder, and Pancreas

The **liver**, **gallbladder**, and **pancreas** are all important accessory organs of digestion. *(See Fig. 29)* Although food products do not pass directly through these organs during the digestive process, they contribute important products and functions to further the breakdown of food.

The **liver** is the largest gland in the body. It is situated in the upper right portion of the abdomen, and its functions are vital to life. One of the main functions of the liver is the production of **bile,** a digestive juice which is transported to the duodenum through the bile ducts. This exocrine secretion of the liver is involved in emulsifying fat globules, or breaking them down into smaller particles so additional digestive enzymes can effectively work on them. When no digestive activity is occurring, the bile produced in the liver backs up through the cystic duct into the gallbladder, or bile sac, which is a small, sac-like structure attached to the inferior surface of the liver. In the gallbladder bile is concentrated and stored for future use in the small intestine. When fat-containing food products pass into the duodenum, hormones are triggered which cause the gallbladder to contract and release the bile into the digestive tract.

Besides the production of bile for digestion, the liver has several other important functions, including the following:

1. helps detoxify the bloodstream by breaking down poisonous materials. An example is the formation of urea by the liver, which is produced as a result of nitrogenous waste products being created during protein metabolism by the cells of the body. The liver then secretes the urea directly into the bloodstream, to be eventually eliminated by the kidneys.

2. phagocytosis of worn out red blood cells and some bacteria

3. produces anticoagulants such as heparin, and other plasma proteins such as albumin, prothrombin, and fibrinogen

4. filters nutrients, particularly sugars, from the blood for storage and future use in the body

5. stores other vitamins and minerals for body use

The pancreas is also situated in the upper abdomen, behind the greater curvature of the stomach, with its head nestled into the curve of the duodenum, and its tail trailing off to the left. The pancreas is classified as a heterocrine gland because it produces both endocrine and exocrine secretions. The endocrine secretion of the pancreas is **insulin,** which is given off directly into the bloodstream, and is important in the metabolizing of carbohydrates by the cells of the body. Specialized groups of cells within the pancreas called the **Islets of Langerhans** are responsible for secreting insulin. The exocrine secretion of the pancreas is a digestive enzyme called **pancreatic juice**, which travels through the pancreatic duct to join up with the common bile duct just before emptying into the duodenum. The small structure formed by the union of the pancreatic duct and the common bile duct is referred to as the **hepatopancreatic duct**, or sometimes the "ampulla of Vater".

The Large Intestine

As we mentioned earlier, the small intestine terminated in the lower right abdomen by emptying into the first part of the large intestine. *(See Fig. 31)* The **large intestine** is approximately five feet in length, and is generally sub-divided into four main segments. The first of these is called the **cecum,** from which we get the name of the opening and valve where the ileum of the small intestine empties its products: the ileo-cecal valve. Attached to the cecum is a small (2-3"), blind pouch called the **vermiform** (L.=worm-like) **appendix.** Inflammation of this structure is the common condition called appendicitis, which often results in surgical removal of the appendix.

The second, and by far the longest, segment of the large intestine is called the **colon.** The colon in turn is divided into four sub-sections identified as follows:

1. **ascending colon** - located on the right side of the abdomen, from the cecum up toward the liver

2. **transverse colon** - across the upper abdomen, from the area of the liver over toward the spleen in the upper left abdomen

3. **descending colon** - down the left side of the abdomen

4. **sigmoid colon** - from the lower left part of the abdomen over to the midline of the body, where it terminates by joining the rectum

The **rectum** is the third part of the large intestine, and is generally about 7 -8" in length. It terminates by joining the fourth and final segment which is known as the **anal canal**. The external opening of the anal canal, where waste products leave the body, is called the **anus.**

In discussing the small intestine, it was indicated that most nutrients are absorbed through its walls, so that by the time the contents of the digestive tract reach the large intestine, nutrient absorption is mostly complete. However, some vitamins are synthesized by bacterial activity in the large intestine and are absorbed into the bloodstream. For the most part, the large intestine serves to absorb additional moisture through its walls and into the bloodstream, so it performs an important function in maintaining proper fluid balance in the body. Some diseases of the large intestine, such as various inflammations, can result in the rapid passage of the contents of the large intestine without a chance for proper moisture absorption to occur. In cases such as this, diarrhea occurs, and a person can become rapidly dehydrated due to a loss of fluid in the body. Conversely, if the contents of the large intestine remain in place too long, allowing excessive moisture absorption to occur, the condition called constipation may occur. The semi-solid substance which results from additional water being absorbed from the digestive residue is referred to as **feces,** which in turn is eliminated from the body through the anus.

The Peritoneum

The **peritoneum** is a thin, slippery serous membrane which lines the abdominal-pelvic cavity. It is made up of two layers of tissue, identified as the parietal and visceral layers. The parietal layer lines the walls of the cavity, and the visceral layer covers over most of the abdominal organs. The space which exists between the parietal and visceral layers of peritoneum is called the **peritoneal cavity**. If you recall, serous membranes were defined as those lining closed body cavities, and secreting a watery lubricating fluid called serum. In the case of the peritoneum, this friction reducing function allows the surrounding organs which it covers to slide easily against one another during movements associated with the digestive process.

Two special subdivisions of the peritoneum are the **mesentery** and the **greater omentum**. The mesentery serves to anchor the intestines to the posterior abdominal wall, and also transmits blood vessels, lymphatics, and nerves to and from the intestines. The greater omentum is an extension of the visceral peritoneum surrounding the stomach and transverse colon, and hangs down like an apron covering over the intestines. *(See Fig. 30)*

THE URINARY SYSTEM
Chapter 6

Daily metabolism which occurs at the cellular level of the body results in the production of various waste products, including carbon dioxide, nitrogenous wastes, ammonia, etc. These waste products must be removed from the body to prevent them from building up to toxic levels. This important function of cleaning waste products out of the blood is the job of the urinary system. In addition to eliminating waste products, the urinary system is also responsible for maintaining proper levels of fluids and salts in the bloodstream, as well as controlling the acid-base balance of the blood. Consequently, we can see that the urinary system is extremely important to achieving proper homeostasis in the body, and must operate in its intended manner if a state of health is to be maintained.

The Kidneys

The **kidneys** are the chief organs of the urinary system, and it is within them that the all important functions of blood filtration are performed. *(See Fig. 32)* The kidneys allow removal of unwanted wastes, water, and ions, while retaining desirable substances and returning them to the blood. The other organs of the urinary system serve as temporary storage locations or transportation structures for removing urine from the body.

The kidneys are located just above the waistline, in the back of the abdominal cavity, and are somewhat protected posteriorly by the eleventh and twelfth pairs of ribs. They are shaped like kidney beans, and are not real large in size, measuring approximately four inches high, two inches wide, and one inch thick. In reference to the vertebrae, the kidneys are generally located at about the level of T-12 to L-3, with the left one being slightly higher than the right due to the large amount of room occupied by the liver in the abdominal cavity. The kidneys are also situated behind the peritoneal sack, and are therefore often described as being **retroperitoneal** organs.

By observing a picture of the kidney, we can readily see that it contains a convex lateral margin and a concave medial margin. The concavity on the medial side of the kidney is called the **hilum** or **hilus.** Through the hilum is where all structures, such as blood vessels, nerves, and the ureters, enter and leave the kidney. The outer surface of the kidney is covered over with a fibrous capsule and a layer of adipose tissue referred to as the perirenal fat pad. These structures help to cushion and protect the kidney and to hold it firmly in place in the abdominal cavity.

A coronal section of the kidney reveals its major internal subdivisions. *(See Fig. 32)* The **cortex,** from the Latin word for "bark", is the outer layer of the kidney. The inner layer is referred to as the **medulla.** In turn, the medulla contains a number of triangular shaped subdivisions, which are somewhat striated in appearance, called the renal pyramids. The base, or wide part of the pyramid, faces the cortex and the apex of the pyramid points toward the center of the kidney.

The **kidney pelvis** is the upper, expanded part of the **ureter,** and serves as a collecting basin for urine which is to be funneled out of the kidney. *(See Fig. 32)* The smaller branches or subdivisions of the pelvis are termed **calyces** (calyx, sing.) from the Greek word meaning "cup of a flower". It is into these calyces that the renal pyramids converge.

Microscopically, the cortex and medulla of the kidney contain hundreds of thousands of structures referred to as **nephrons.** *(See Fig. 32)* These nephrons are the functional units of kidney tissue, and serve to perform the previously mentioned functions of filtering the bloodstream. A nephron has two main parts, called the **renal corpuscle** and the **renal tubule**. The renal corpuscle is a structure composed of a minute, cup-like structure called Bowman's capsule, which contains within it a tuft of specialized capillaries known as a **glomerulus.** The renal tubule is a long and twisted tail-like structure attached to Bowman's capsule. A closer look at the diagram of a nephron is important to understand how these structures are arranged so that we may better see how they function to cleanse the bloodstream.

The functional process performed by the nephrons is often divided into three main activities: filtration, re-absorption, and secretion.

The process of **filtration** begins by blood entering the capsule through a vessel called the afferent arteriole, where it proceeds into the glomerulus. It is important to notice that the blood vessel leaving the capsule, the efferent arteriole, is smaller in diameter than the blood vessel which brought the blood into the area. This means that glomerular blood pressure remains relatively high so that filtration may occur. Through the walls of the glomeruli, water and waste products are filtered out of the blood and into Bowman's capsule. This process of filtration occurs at the rate of approximately 180 liters per day! Certainly this much water is not lost through the urinary system, as most of it is recaptured in the second phase of the process called re-absorption.

Re-absorption occurs in the renal tubules, which the filtered substances pass into after leaving Bowman's capsule. Through the walls of the renal tubules, most of the water filtered out of the glomeruli (about 178 liters per day) is re-absorbed into the capillaries surrounding the outside of the tubules. Other desired substances such as glucose, potassium, and some of the sodium ions are also re-absorbed. If this re-absorption does not occur as it should due to various disease conditions, the body can lose too much fluid through the urinary system and become seriously dehydrated.

The final phase of urine formation is called **secretion.** Secretion can be thought of as the opposite of re-absorption, because in secretion, substances are moving out of the capillaries around the renal tubules and into the residual urine passing through these tubules. Substances which are secreted out of the bloodstream into the renal tubules include ammonia, hydrogen ions, and even certain drugs. In this way, secretion into the renal tubules helps maintain the proper acid-base balance in the body.

Several hormones produced in the body have a regulatory effect on the renal tubules and the manner in which they function. For example, a hormone which is secreted by the posterior part of the pituitary gland has the effect of making the renal tubules more permeable, thus allowing normal re-absorption of water back into the bloodstream. Without this hormone, too much water would pass out of the body through the urinary system. Consequently, this pituitary hormone is referred to as an anti-diuretic hormone. Also, hormones put off by the adrenal cortex (aldosterone) and by specialized cells in the walls of the atria of the heart (atrial natriuretic hormone) have an effect on the proper levels of sodium which are absorbed from or secreted into the renal tubules. Together these hormones have an important balancing effect on the homeostasis of body fluids.

Other Urinary System Organs

The **ureters** are the tubes which convey urine out of the kidney and down to the urinary bladder. *(See Fig. 34)* As was mentioned earlier, they begin as a narrowing of the funnel-like kidney pelvis, and are generally about 10-12 inches long. As is the case with food moving through the digestive tract, smooth muscle contractions in the walls of the ureters called peristalsis help to move the urine along its course.

The **urinary bladder** is a reservoir for urine awaiting periodic discharge from the body. *(See Fig. 34)* The walls of the bladder contain much smooth muscle and elastic fibers, which allow it to expand considerably in order to hold varying amounts of urine. The average capacity of the urinary bladder is about 700-800 milliliters (ml). When about 200-400 ml accumulate, receptors in the bladder wall transmit impulses to the central nervous system and initiate the conscious desire to void urine. The term micturition is given to the process of eliminating urine from the body.

The **urethra** is the tube which carries urine out of the urinary bladder to the outside of the body. *(See Fig. 34)* Like the rest of the urinary system it is lined with mucous membrane. The urethra exits the inferior portion of the bladder, and in the female body it is only about 1 1/2 inches long, opening near the anterior wall of the vagina. In the male, the urethra averages about 8 inches in length, as it must first pass through the prostate gland as it leaves the bladder, then traverse through the penis. Also, in the male body the urethra serves the dual function of transporting spermatozoa to the outside. Therefore, it is considered part of both the urinary and reproductive systems.

Urinalysis is an important diagnostic tool to indicate various disease processes in the body. Urine is normally about 95% water and 5% waste products, such as urea, uric acid, and ammonia. Many tests can be run on urine samples to determine an individual's relative state of health. For example, abnormal quantities of glucose, serum albumin, blood, hemoglobin, or pus indicate pathological conditions which warrant closer medical attention.

Not all waste products are eliminated through the digestive and urinary systems in the human body. Some organs in the body are often described as accessory organs of excretion because they help to eliminate excess quantities of various substances. For example, the lungs eliminate the waste gas carbon dioxide with each breath you exhale, and the skin helps to eliminate excess water, salt, and some urea through the process of sweating. Also, the liver is indirectly helping to eliminate nitrogenous waste products from the body by forming urea from these products and then releasing it into the bloodstream for the kidneys to filter out.

THE REPRODUCTIVE SYSTEM
Chapter 7

The reproductive system is responsible for the production of new life within a species. Human reproduction is said to be sexual reproduction because a parent of each sex produces a specialized reproductive cell called a gamete. The male gamete is the spermatozoa and the female gamete is called an ovum. When these sex cells combine in a process called fertilization, the process of new life formation begins. The organs of the male and female reproductive systems are responsible for producing, bringing together, and nurturing these reproductive cells until a new birth eventually occurs.

Male Reproductive Organs

The **testes** are the main, essential organs of the male reproductive system which are responsible for the production of **spermatozoa,** the male sex cells. In addition to spermatozoa, the testes produce a hormone called **testosterone,** which has to do with stimulating various bodily functions or characteristics. For example, testosterone is said to be the "masculinizing" hormone, as it influences the development of the accessory organs of reproduction and secondary sexual characteristics such as male body hair distribution and the deepening of the male voice at puberty. Testosterone also has an important effect on protein anabolism in the body, which directly reflects upon the greater muscular development normally seen in men.

The **testes** are paired, oval shaped glands, contained within the **scrotum,** which is a sack of loose skin and fascia suspended from the lower anterior pelvic wall. *(See Fig. 35)* This location of the testes within the scrotum, outside of the abdominal-pelvic cavity, is significant in that the proper development of spermatozoa is partially dependent upon a temperature range about one to three degrees Centigrade cooler than that of the pelvic cavity. In cases where the testes do not descend into the scrotum from the pelvic cavity, as is normal in a male child, failure to medically or surgically correct this condition may result in sterility due to the inability of spermatozoa to grow and mature in this warmer environment.

Two layers of tissue covering the outer surface of the testes include an inner dense fibrous capsule called the tunica albuginea, and an outer serous membrane referred to as the tunica vaginalis. The tunica vaginalis is essentially an "outpocketing" of peritoneum which covered the testes while developing up in the pelvic cavity prior to birth.

Internally, the testes are subdivided into numerous (200-300) smaller lobules, each of which contains tightly coiled structures called **seminiferous tubules**. These tubules are important because it is from their inner linings that spermatozoa are produced. This process which immature cells progress through before they become mature spermatozoa is called **spermatogenesis.** A mature spermatozoon contains three main parts, including a head or body, which contains twenty-three chromosomes, representing all of the father's genetic material, a mid-piece, and a whip-like tail which aids in locomotion as the spermatozoon moves through the female reproductive tract. Spermatozoa also contain enzymes which help enable them to penetrate the outer layers of an ovum if fertilization is to occur.

Spermatozoa which were produced in the testes will eventually move out of the seminiferous tubules and into the first portion of the spermatic duct called the **epididymis.** *(See Fig. 35)* The epididymis is a tightly coiled and twisted structure which lies against the posterior surface of the testes. Spermatozoa continue their maturing process as they pass through this lengthy section of the spermatic duct. Although the epididymis is only about 1 1/2 inches long in its coiled state, it is so tightly coiled that if straightened out it would be approximately twenty feet in length!

The second section of the spermatic duct, called the **ductus (vas) deferens**, is about 18 inches in length. *(See Fig. 35)* It begins as a straightening out of the epididymis near the lower border of the testis, ascends up and out of the scrotum, enters the pelvic cavity, passes over the top of the urinary bladder, and ends up near the posterior inferior part of the bladder. The vas deferens delivers spermatozoa toward the last section of the spermatic duct, and eventually the urethra via peristaltic contractions in its muscular walls during the process of discharging semen.

The third and final segment of the spermatic duct is called the **ejaculatory duct** and it is only about one inch in length. *(See Fig. 35)* The ejaculatory duct empties semen into the urethra. The urethra is the tube which originates at the urinary bladder and terminates at the external urethral orifice at the tip of the penis, and serves to transport urine from the bladder to the outside of the body. Due to the fact that it also transports semen to the outside, in the male body the urethra may be considered part of both the urinary and the reproductive systems.

There are several accessory glands in the male reproductive system which are involved in adding secretions to the spermatozoa and forming the end product referred to as **semen** or **seminal fluid**. The first of these structures are called the seminal vesicles, which are small pouches located near the point where the vas deferens terminates. In fact, the duct out of the seminal vesicle joins with the vas deferens to form the ejaculatory duct. The fluid produced by these glands helps to transport and nourish the spermatozoa.

The **prostate gland** is an organ which encircles the urethra just inferior to the bladder. *(See Fig. 35)* The prostate adds a secretion to the seminal fluid which is believed to help activate the spermatozoa.

Finally, small glands referred to as the **bulbourethral** (Cowper's) **glands** lie inferior to the prostate gland. *(See Fig. 35)* They also add an alkaline secretion to the seminal fluid which helps to buffer the acidity of the male urethra and the female reproductive tract.

The **penis** is the male reproductive organ designed to deliver spermatozoa into the female reproductive tract. *(See Fig. 35)* It consists of a shaft which terminates in an enlarged tip called the **glans.** Covering over the glans is a retractable layer of skin referred to as the **prepuce** or foreskin. This section of skin is often surgically removed in a process called **circumcision.**

Internally the penis consists primarily of three columns of spongy, erectile tissue which become engorged with blood during sexual excitation, causing the penis to enlarge and become rigid. This is referred to as erection. The two larger columns of tissue are called the **corpora cavernosa**, and the third section, surrounding the penile urethra, is known as the **corpus spongiosum.**

Female Reproductive Organs

The two ovaries are the essential organs of the female reproductive system, and are located in the pelvic cavity, attached by ligaments to the pelvic wall. Like the testes, the ovaries are considered heterocrine glands because they produce both an exocrine product (ova) and endocrine secretions, or **hormones.**

Oogenesis refers to the process of egg or **ova (sing.=ovum)** formation which occurs in the ovaries. Every female child is born with approximately 1,000,000 immature egg cells, but only about 350-500 of these cells develops into mature ova during a woman's reproductive years. Those eggs which eventually reach the mature stage within the ovary are contained within a tiny sac-like structure referred to as the **Graafian follicle**. Under the influence of hormones, one of these mature follicles ruptures through the wall of the ovary each month, expelling an ovum, in a process called **ovulation.** After ovulation occurs, the ruptured follicle progresses through additional stages prior to eventually degenerating completely.

Estrogen and **progesterone** are the two female hormones produced by the ovaries. Estrogen is often referred to as the "feminizing" hormone, as it is responsible for the development of female sex characteristics, such as the development and maturing of the genitals, the growth of pubic hair, and initiation of the menstrual cycle. Progesterone works in concert with estrogen in several ways, including having an effect on the menstrual cycle and preparing the mammary glands for milk production. Progesterone also stimulates the proliferation of epithelial cells lining the uterus in preparation for implantation of a fertilized egg.

The **fallopian tubes**, also known as **uterine tubes** or **oviducts,** are structures which serve as passageways for an ovum to reach the uterus. *(See Fig. 36)* The fallopian tubes extend laterally out from the top of the uterus (about 4 inches), with their open ends lying adjacent to the ovaries. The funnel-shaped end of a fallopian tube, called the infundibulum, contains fringe-like projections called fimbriae. When ovulation occurs into the abdominal cavity, the waving fimbriae create currents which attract the ovum into the fallopian tube. The inside of the tube is also lined with ciliated epithelial cells, which help move the ovum along toward the uterus.

The fallopian tube also serves as the normal point of fertilization. If a sper-

51

matozoon is able to swim up through the female reproductive tract, reach the fallopian tube, and reach the point where the ovum is located, fertilization may occur. The normal location for fertilization to occur is in the outer 1/3 of the fallopian tube. A fertilized ovum, which is referred to as a zygote, now contains the genetic material from both parents, and soon begins to divide and grow, creating a new life. It generally takes about ten days for a zygote to proceed through the fallopian tube and implant itself on the inner lining of the uterus, where it will continue to grow and mature over the ensuing nine month period.

The **uterus** is the female organ which serves as the point of development of a fetus during the period of gestation (L.="to bear"), the time from conception to birth. *(See Fig. 36)* It is often described as an inverted, pear-shaped organ, situated behind the urinary bladder and in front of the rectum. It is mainly a muscular organ, but it actually has three distinct layers, identified as follows:

1. **endometrium** - the specialized inner lining, which is functionally involved in proliferating and developing into components necessary to sustain fetal life if pregnancy occurs. *(See Fig. 36)* The endometrium also sheds its outer lining, along with natural bleeding, during the monthly menstrual period if fertilization and implantation do not occur.

2. **myometrium** - the middle, muscular layer, consisting of thick, smooth muscle tissue. *(See Fig. 36)*

3. **perimetrium** - the serous outer lining around the uterus, which is actually visceral peritoneum. *(See Fig. 36)*

The uterus has several gross subdivisions which are readily apparent by examining a picture of the organ. The upper, dome-shaped portion is called the **fundus** (L.=base), the main central portion is the **body,** and the constricted, neck-like inferior part, which opens into the vagina, is referred to as the **cervix** (L.=neck). *(See Fig. 36)*

The **vagina** (L.=sheath), also known as the birth canal, is the muscular passageway from the uterus to the outside of the body. *(See Fig. 36)* In addition, it serves as the passageway for the entrance of the male penis during sexual intercourse, and permits the passage of menstrual flow out of the body.

The external female genitals are collectively referred to as the vulva. Included in the vulva are the following structures:

1. **mons pubis** - the area of adipose tissue and skin, covered with pubic hair, which overlies the pubic bone

2. **labia majora** - the two folds of skin, running inferiorly and posteriorly from the mons pubis, and enclosing the additional structures listed below *(See Fig. 37)*

3. **labia minora** - the two smaller folds of tissue, covering the entranceway into the vagina *(See Fig. 37)*

52

4. **urethral orifice** - the opening into the urethra, just anterior to the vaginal orifice *(See Fig. 37)*

5. **clitoris** - a mass of highly sensitive erectile tissue, located at the anterior junction of the labia minora *(See Fig. 37)*

6. **hymen** - a thin mucous membrane which partially covers the entrance into the vagina

7. **vestibule** - the entranceway into the vagina, between the two labia minora

In addition to the internal and external genitals of the female, the **mammary glands**, or breasts, are also considered accessory organs of reproduction. The breasts lie anterior to the pectoral muscles of the thorax, and are attached to them by connective tissue. The anterior surface of each breast contains a circular, pigmented area called the areola, surrounding a protruding nipple.

Internally, the mammary glands contain 15-20 lobes in a radial arrangement around the nipple. The subdivisions within these lobes contain the milk secreting glands. When milk is being produced, it is secreted from these glands through a series of ducts ending up in the nipple. Also embedded within the breast are varying amounts of adipose tissue which essentially determines the size of the breast.

The **menstrual cycle** refers to a series of changes which occur in the female reproductive organs, under the stimulation of certain anterior pituitary hormones, which in turn have an effect on the levels of estrogen and progesterone produced by the ovaries. Although there is often considerable variation in the length of the phases of the menstrual cycle from woman to woman, a typical cycle is based on a 28 day time frame.

Days 1-5 of the cycle are referred to as the menstrual period. During this time, as a result of decreasing hormone levels, the epithelial lining of the uterus is shed, along with natural bleeding, which passes out through the cervix of the uterus and the vagina.

In the post-menstrual phase, or days 6-13, the lining of the uterus begins to repair itself, while immature eggs are beginning to mature within the ovaries. Eventually one ovum develops into a mature follicle, referred to as a **Graafian follicle**, and on day 14 of the cycle it erupts through the wall of the ovary in a process called ovulation. This ovum will migrate into the fallopian tube where fertilization may occur if spermatozoa are present. Thus it can be said that ovulation occurs 14 days after the beginning of the menstrual period, or conversely, 14 days before the beginning of the next menstrual period in a 28 day cycle. This is a critical time during the cycle, as the ovum lives only a short period of time after ovulation, and spermatozoa live only several days after entering the female reproductive tract. Therefore, the window of time for successful fertilization to occur is rather short each month.

The pre-menstrual phase, or days 15-28 of the cycle, represent the time during which the uterine lining is once again being prepared to receive a fertilized ovum. The endometrium grows thicker and becomes more vascular in anticipation of implantation occurring. If implantation of a fertilized ovum occurs, pregnancy takes place, and the development of a new life begins. However, if implantation does not occur, hormone levels drop, and after the 28th day of the cycle, another menstrual phase will begin.

THE RESPIRATORY SYSTEM
Chapter 8

The act of breathing and the process of respiration are often thought to be one and the same. Although the two processes are interrelated, they are actually quite different from one another.

The act of **breathing** is a physical process in which air is pulled from the environment into the lungs by the contraction of the diaphragm, or phrenic muscle, followed shortly thereafter by the pushing of air from the lungs into the environment due to the relaxation of the diaphragm. Words like inhaling and inspiration are relative to the pulling of air into the respiratory system while exhaling and expiration are related to the pushing out of air from the respiratory system. One can "breathe" through the nose or the mouth since these cavities are both connected to a part of the respiratory system commonly called the throat or pharynx, but normal breathing occurs through the nose. Breathing is primarily an involuntary act but can be controlled consciously. A person can deliberately stop breathing or hold their breath. A person can also increase the volume of a breath (as in deep breathing) as well as increase the rhythm of the breaths (as in rapid breathing).

Respiration, on the other hand, is the process by which the body exchanges the oxygen from the inspired air for the carbon dioxide manufactured by the cells during metabolism. Respiration is involuntary in nature and the amount or rate of respiration is dependent upon the activity level of the body. The higher the amount of activity, the higher the need for oxygen and the higher production of carbon dioxide. The purpose of the respiratory system is to maintain a constant supply of oxygen to the cells and to remove the carbon dioxide produced by the cells. The respiratory system and the circulatory system work together because it is the erythrocytes in the blood stream which act as the vehicles by which the exchange is made.

The process of respiration takes place in two distinct locations. The exchange of metabolic gases (oxygen and carbon dioxide) which occurs at the level of the capillary beds of the lungs is called **external respiration**. Here oxygen is taken in by red blood cells, and carbon dioxide is given off. Respiration that takes place when red cells give up oxygen to individual body cells, and take on carbon dioxide, is called **internal respiration**. Blood which is rich in oxygen can be referred to as oxygenated blood, arterialized blood or pure blood. Blood which is rich in carbon dioxide is called de-oxygenated blood, venous blood or impure blood.

The respiratory system consists of six distinct organs arranged in a specific order. These organs include the **nose, pharynx, larynx, trachea, bronchi, and the lungs.** (*See Fig. 38*)

Organs of the Respiratory System:

The respiratory system consists of six organs: nose, pharynx, larynx, trachea, bronchi, and lungs.

The Nose

The **nose** is actually two separate structures, one behind the other. The part of the "nose" which people are familiar with protrudes away from the skull. The other part of the "nose" is a triangular cavity visible only on a skull which has been cleaned of all fleshy material.

The framework of the protruding part of the nose is made of cartilage covered with skin and lined with mucous epithelial membrane. The dorsum, wings and tip of the nose are formed from **alar cartilage**.

Oval shaped holes called **anterior nares**, located at the base of the nose provide an entrance way into this part of the nose. The alar cartilage is held away from the skull by a piece of **septal cartilage**. This septal cartilage helps form the vertical **nasal septum** which divides the nose into right and left chambers.

The **nasal cavity** is that part of the nose which creates a hole in the skull below and between the orbital cavities. *(See Fig. 39)* Various bones of the face and cranium form the nasal cavity. The cavity is formed by the right and left nasal bones, right and left maxillary bones, the ethmoid bone, the sphenoid bone, and the vomer bone.

The nasal cavity is somewhat reduced in size by the right and left inferior nasal conchae bones which protrude medially from the inner walls of the right and left maxillary bones. The inspired air will exit the nasal cavity through two oval shaped holes called the **posterior nares.**

The nasal cavity is divided into two separate chambers by the vomer bone and the perpendicular plate of the ethmoid bone. The nasal cavity is surrounded by small nearly-closed holes in the bones called **sinuses.** Collectively the sinuses are known as the **paranasal sinuses.** This group of cavities includes the ethmoid sinuses, sphenoid sinuses, frontal sinuses and maxillary sinuses.

The nose functions in several ways. The mucous membranes, and hairs contained within the nasal cavity, filter the inspired air of pollutants such as dust and pollen. The moisture rich mucous lining of the nose and nasal cavity also humidify the inspired air. Diffusion takes place best in a moist environment. The highly vascularized mucous membrane also act to regulate the temperature of the inspired air by either removing or adding heat to the air. Diffusion is best at the normal body temperature of thirty-seven degrees Celsius. The nasal cavity also contains sensory nerves, called olfactory nerves, which detect odors.

Normal breathing channels the air in the nasal cavity into an inverted cone-shaped structure called the **pharynx.** *(See Fig. 39)* The pharynx is subdivided into three portions. That portion which lies just posterior to the posterior nares and superior to the oral cavity is called the **nasopharynx.** The nasopharynx can be obstructed by inflamed adenoid glands, sometimes producing a phenomena of mouth breathing. Small canals called Eustachian tubes connect the pharynx with the inner ears. The middle portion of the pharynx is called the **oropharynx.** The oropharynx is located posterior of the oral cavity. This area normally contains the tonsils. When the tonsils are infected, a person has difficulty swallowing.

The most inferior portion of the pharynx is called the **laryngopharynx.** This section is so named because it is located just superior of the larynx (voicebox). The pharynx is also considered to be part of the digestive system. At the bottom of the pharynx, food and liquids are channeled into the esophagus and air is channeled into the larynx. The walls of the pharynx are made of an inner layer of mucous epithelial membrane, a middle supportive layer of fibrous connective tissue, and an outer layer of muscle which produces the peristaltic waves characteristic of swallowing.

The Larynx

The **larynx** is a cartilaginous structure known as the voicebox. *(See Fig. 39)* The larynx is composed of three distinct pieces of cartilage. The most superior piece of cartilage is a leaf-shaped structure called the **epiglottis.** The epiglottis acts as a trap-door over the top of the main body of the larynx. The epiglottis is forced downward over the opening into the larynx (the glottis) by the tongue when swallowing occurs, preventing food and liquid from entering into the voicebox.

The anterior and lateral walls of the larynx are formed by a shield-shaped piece of cartilage called the **thyroid cartilage**. *(See Fig. 39)* This piece of cartilage is so-named because the thyroid gland is located near its inferior border. The protrusion commonly called the **Adam's Apple** is located on the thyroid cartilage. This protrusion marks the anterior attachment of the true vocal cords on the interior wall of the thyroid cartilage.

The most inferior portion of the larynx is made from a ring-shaped piece of cartilage called the **cricoid cartilage**. The inferior edge of the cricoid cartilage marks the beginning of the trachea.

The entrance into the larynx is called the **glottis.** At this location the internal diameter of the larynx is approximately one inch. The entrance is further restricted by protruding pieces of cartilage called **false vocal cords,** and by **true vocal cords**, which are bands of ligament-like elastic tissue, effectively reducing the size of the opening. *(See Fig. 39)* True vocal cords are important in the production of sound. The entry way is restricted to a distance of about one-eighth of an inch. Usually large particles of food cannot enter into the larynx and obstruct the airway. This narrow space between the true vocal cords is called the **rima glottis.**

The normal growth rate of the larynx is affected by the release of hormones at puberty. Typically the male shows a more pronounced amount of growth during puberty than the female. The result of this rapid growth may be a high pitched voice in the male for a period of time until the true vocal cords catch up with the increasing diameter of the larynx. Like the pharynx, the larynx is lined with mucous epithelial membrane with supportive walls of a fibro-muscular nature.

The Trachea

The **trachea** is commonly known as the windpipe. *(See Fig. 38)* The trachea is located immediately below the larynx, part in the cervical region and part in the thoracic cavity. It is about four and one-half inches in length. The trachea is an anatomical tube consisting of a stack of C-shaped cartilage rings lined with mucous membrane. A small amount of soft tissue separates each ring. The surgical procedure of a tracheotomy relies on these small spaces of soft tissue for the insertion of a breathing tube into an obstructed airway.

The Bronchi, Bronchioles and Alveoli

The trachea bifurcates into two separate tubes called the right and left **primary** or **principle bronchi.** *(See Fig. 38)* These tubes resemble the trachea in all aspects except they are smaller in diameter. Each principle bronchi further divides into **secondary** or **lobe bronchi.** The left principle bronchus divides into two lobe bronchi and the right principle bronchus divides into three lobe bronchi. This division is relative to the number of lobes in the two lungs. Each lobe bronchi further divides into a number of **segmental bronchioles.** Bronchioles are smaller in internal diameter than bronchi. Each segmental bronchiole will divide once again into numerous **terminal bronchioles.** The combined space of the terminal bronchioles is sometimes called the atria of the lungs. At the end of each terminal bronchiole is a small globe-shaped structure called an **alveolus** or **alveolar sac.** External respiration diffusion takes place in the alveolar sac. At this point the lungs resemble a cluster of grapes on a supporting vine.

The Lungs

The **lungs** are actually millions of alveolar sacs held together in the triangular shape by an epithelial membrane called the **pleura.** The layer of pleura which surrounds and defines the shape of each lung is called **visceral pleura.** Another layer of pleura lines the cavity which houses the lungs. This pleura is called **parietal pleura.** The right and left lungs differ in that the right lung is slightly larger and contains three lobes, while the left is made up of only two lobes. The left lung also contains an indentation on its medial inferior surface called the **cardiac notch**. The heart lies against the lung in this area, forming the indentation.

Healthy lung tissue in newborn infants is very light, thin and highly elastic. The lungs have a pale pink color due to the presence of red blood cells around the alveolar sacs. Over a period of years, dust and other pollutants may change this color to a dark gray by adulthood.

The volume of air that passes in and out of the lungs over a lifetime is categorized in several ways:

1. *Minimal Air Volume*: the volume of air inhaled in the newborns first breath. This air remains in the lungs to keep them inflated.

2. *Tidal Air Volume*: the volume of air inspired and expired during normal breathing. The normal breathing rate is eighteen breaths per minute when the body is at rest.

3. *Complemental Air Volume*: the volume of air which can be inspired into the lungs in addition to the tidal air volume. This volume is relative to the concept of deep breathing.

4. *Supplemental Air Volume*: the volume of air which can be expired out of the lungs in addition to the tidal air volume.

5. *Residual Air Volume*: the volume of air which remains in the lungs after the supplemental air volume is exhaled. This volume of air cannot be exhaled and it helps to keep the lungs inflated. A collapsed lung has somehow lost its residual air volume.

THE CIRCULATORY SYSTEM
Chapter 9

A one-celled organism lives in an aqueous environment. In this environment are found the oxygen and food necessary to maintain the life of the cell and into it the cell excretes the waste products of its metabolism. Remove the cell from this fluid environment and it dies.

The cells of multicellular organisms, including the human, are no less dependent upon a fluid environment. Their environment is the body's tissue fluid, an intercellular material that provides for their needs. Without the tissue fluid the cells soon die.

The tissue fluid is a part of the body's internal environment, yet it is far removed from the external environment from which it must receive the materials to sustain the life of the cell. The bridge between the external and internal environments is the **circulatory system.**

The circulatory system consists of the heart as a pump, and an extensive network of tubes throughout the body which contain a fluid for the transportation of essential substances to and from the cells of the body, and the removal of various waste substances from these cells. The circulatory system is frequently divided into the blood vascular system, which includes the blood, heart and blood vessels; and the lymphatic system, which includes the lymph, lymph vessels and lymph nodes. The study of the circulatory system is called **angiology.**

Functions of the Circulatory System

The functions of the circulatory system can be categorized into three major areas: transportation, regulation, and protection.

The **transportation function** of the blood involves the movement of all the substances necessary for cellular metabolism throughout the circulatory system.

The movement of the respiratory gases oxygen and carbon dioxide is accomplished by the red blood cells, or **erythrocytes.** In the lungs, oxygen from inspired air attaches to the hemoglobin in red blood cells, to then be carried to the cells throughout the body. At the same time, the waste product of cellular metabolism, carbon dioxide, is released by the erythrocytes and carried from the lungs in expired air.

The movement of nutritive substances throughout the body by the circulatory system is a vital part of its transportation function. Within the plasma of the blood many of the digested nutrients taken into our body are dissolved and carried to the cells throughout the body. Such things as carbohydrates and sugars, fats, proteins, vitamins, and minerals are all carried by the circulatory system.

The movement of waste products is equally important to the body's well being. The breakdown of proteins through metabolism produces nitrogen-containing compounds that must be eliminated from the body. These are carried from their source of production in the cells to the kidneys, where they are filtered out of the blood. Excessive water and certain salts are also carried to the skin for their eventual elimination.

The **regulation function** of the blood involves the maintaining of the pH of the body through buffers dissolved in the blood and amino acids of proteins. The circulatory system, in conjunction with the urinary system, regulates the amount of water and salts in the blood. The integumentary system and the circulatory system also help to maintain the body's temperature by the dispersion of heat from the muscles of the body. Some of this heat maintains normal body temperature, while excess heat is dissipated through the skin into the atmosphere.

The **protective function** of the blood involves the circulatory system's ability to respond to injury as well as its ability to defend against foreign substances in the body. The clotting mechanism protects against loss of blood, while **leukocytes,** or white blood cells, are specialized to fight off infections.

Hematology

Hematology is the study of the blood. Blood is the highly specialized, viscous connective tissue that circulates though the blood vascular system. It contains three types of blood cells, or formed elements, which are suspended in a liquid called **plasma.**

Characteristics of Blood

Blood is red due to the presence of the red blood cells which contain hemoglobin, a specialized oxygen-carrying pigmented protein. The normal temperature of blood is 38 degrees Centigrade or 100.3 degrees Fahrenheit. The specific gravity of blood is between 1.041 and 1.067 (water has a specific gravity of 1). Its viscosity (resistance to flow) is 4½ to 5½ times that of water. The pH or Hydrogen Ion concentration is 7.35 to 7.45, which makes blood slightly alkaline in nature. Blood volume is between 5 to 6 quarts for the average adult, or about 8.5 to 9.0% of body weight.

Components of Blood

Blood is made up of two basic components, a clear straw-colored liquid called **plasma,** and a collection of minute solid particles that are referred to collectively as **formed elements, blood cells,** or **corpuscles.** These formed elements include of three kinds of blood cells: **erythrocytes,** or red blood cells; **leukocytes,** or white blood cells; and **thrombocytes,** or platelets.

About 45 % of the volume of blood in the body is made up of blood cells. The remaining 55% is liquid plasma, containing important blood proteins such as serum albumin, serum globulin, fibrinogen, and other dissolved substances.

Erythrocytes or Red Blood Cells

Red blood cells (RBC), or erythrocytes, are tiny bi-concave discs that lose their nuclei before entering the blood stream. *(See Fig. 40)* Their primary function is the transport of oxygen and carbon dioxide. They pick up oxygen in the lungs which is carried by the **hemoglobin** found in the red blood cells. The presence of iron in the hemoglobin is what gives erythrocytes their characteristic red color. They are only about 7.7 microns in diameter, and are the most numerous of the blood cells, numbering about 4,200,000 to 5,900,000 per mm^3 of blood. Red blood cells are produced in the red marrow of bones.

Red blood cells have a life expectancy ranging up to about 120 days. When blood cells break down, the hemoglobin they contain is converted into other substances by the body. Hemoglobin consists of **heme,** a pigment containing iron, and a protein called **globin.** A reddish-brown pigmented substance called **bilirubin** results from this hemoglobin breakdown. Some of the bilirubin may undergo further chemical changes and be converted into a greenish pigmented substance called **biliverdin.** Bilirubin and biliverdin are pigments which are then eliminated by the liver, stored in the gall bladder, and secreted into the small intestine as needed to aid in the digestive process. When the liver or its ducts become diseased, or fail to operate properly, excess quantities of these pigments may build up in the bloodstream, causing the condition known as **jaundice.**

Leukocytes or White Blood Cells

White blood cells (WBC), or leukocytes, are spherical cells that contain nuclei of varying shapes and sizes. *(See Fig. 40)* Their primary function is defense against infection in the body. They may even leave the blood vascular system to fight infections in the tissues of the body. They may pass through the walls of the capillaries through a process called **diapedesis.** They vary in size, but are larger than red blood cells, averaging about 10 microns in diameter. Their numbers range from 4,300 to 10,800 per mm^3 of blood. Most leukocytes are produced by the red marrow of bones, while the lymphocytes are produced by the lymphatic system.

Leukocytes are subdivided into five different kinds of blood cells, usually grouped in two categories by the characteristics of their cytoplasm (what's inside the cell). Some contain small granules within their cells and are called **granulocytes**, while the ones that do not contain granules are called **agranulocytes.** *(See Fig. 40)* The granulocytes include neutrophils, eosinophils, and basophils. Agranulocytes include lymphocytes and monocytes.

Some of the leukocytes have the ability to seek out foreign substances in the blood, or in the tissue spaces, and engulf the foreign substance through a process called **phagocytosis.** These cells are called **phagocytes.** The white blood cells that are phagocytes are the neutrophils, monocytes, and eosinophils. The lymphocytes are important in the body's immunity, including the production of antibodies, while the basophils are believed to help prevent the intra-vascular blood from clotting by producing heparin.

Thrombocytes or Platelets

Thrombocytes, or **platelets**, are the smallest of the blood cells, varying in size but averaging about 3 microns in diameter. *(See Fig. 40)* They are irregular shaped discs sometimes called cytoplasmic fragments of megakaryocytes from which they are formed. They are produced in the red bone marrow. They are more numerous than the leukocytes, ranging from 150,000 to 350,000 per mm^3 of blood. Their primary function is to help form clots in the walls of broken blood vessels.

Coagulation or Clotting of the Blood

Coagulation, or clotting of the blood, is the result of the action of the blood vessels, blood platelets, and the clotting factors. The blood vessels constitute the body's first line of defense to body injury. In the response to various stimuli, the vessels contract at the site of injury. This causes a decrease in the flow of blood and an aggregation of platelets. The platelets form a plug by adhering to the injured tissue. During this process, the platelets release their contents. These contents are called aggregating agents and are very powerful. Besides attracting more platelets to the injured site, these agents also cause further contraction of the blood vessels and are involved in the activation of the clotting factors. The clotting factors will result in the formation of the fibrin clot.

There are two pathways which will lead to the formation of the fibrin clot. One method is caused by the release of chemicals from injured or damaged tissues, called the extrinsic clotting mechanism. The other is caused by the contact of blood with foreign surfaces in the absence of any injury or tissue damage, and is called the intrinsic clotting mechanism.

Some of the substances found in the blood which may be involved in the clotting of the blood are tissue thromboplastin (Factor III), thrombokinase (Factor X), cephalin (a phospholipid), calcium ions (Factor IV), prothrombin (Factor II), and fibrinogen (Factor I).

Once the clot has formed, the healing process has begun. Following the healing process the clot must be removed. This is accomplished by fibrinolysis of the clot, caused by plasminogen which has been converted into protease plasmin. The clot is slowly broken down and eliminated.

During normal times the blood does not clot due to the presence of several chemical substances which help to maintain the delicate balance between the blood's not clotting and clotting. Substances which inhibit the blood's ability to clot include antithrombin and antiprothrombin (or heparin). They inhibit the formation of thrombin and prothrombin which are parts of the common pathway of either the extrinsic or intrinsic mechanism of blood coagulation.

Plasma

Plasma is the liquid part of blood. It is the material in which we find the formed elements suspended. It also has many other substances dissolved in it.

Plasma contains **water** (92% to 95%) and **dissolved components** (5% to 8%). These disolved components include blood proteins (serum albumin, serum globulin, and fibrinogen); inorganic salts (chlorides, bicarbonates, phosphates, and sulfates) of sodium (Na), potassium (K), calcium (Ca), and magnesium (Mg); nutrients (carbohydrates, such as glucose, fats, proteins, minerals, and vitamins); wastes (urea); respiratory gases of oxygen (O_2), carbon dioxide (CO_2), and nitrogen (N_2); enzymes, hormones, antibodies, and other ingested substances such as alcohol and drugs.

Plasma that has all of the clotting factors removed is called serum. It resembles plasma in that it has a clear amber appearance.

Blood Groupings

Blood grouping, or typing of the blood, is based on the presence or absence of certain agglutinogens (antigens) in the membranes of red blood cells.

The ABO Blood Types

The ABO Blood Grouping is based on the presence (or absence) of two agglutinogens found in the red cell membrane, agglutinogen A and agglutinogen B. Everyone's blood has one of these four combinations of agglutinogens in their red cell membranes: (1) Only A, (2) Only B, (3) Both A and B, or (4) Neither A or B.

A person with only Agglutinogen A is said to have type A blood. A person with only Agglutinogen B is said to have type B blood. A person with both Agglutinogens A and B is said to have type AB blood, while the person who has neither Agglutinogen A or B is said to have type O blood.

The distribution of the ABO blood types in the general population are represented by the following table.

Table K

Blood Type Distribution in Population

Type O — 40 - 43 % Population = **UNIVERSAL DONOR**

Type A — 40 - 45 % Population

Type B — 10 - 15 % Population

Type AB — 4 - 5 % Population = **UNIVERSAL RECIPIENT**

Who can give blood to another?				
	RECIPIENT			
TYPE	**O**	**A**	**B**	**AB**
O	*YES	YES	YES	YES →UNIVERSAL DONOR
A	NO	*YES	NO	YES
B	NO	NO	*YES	YES
AB	NO	NO	NO	*YES

(The left side is labeled vertically: **DONOR**)

↓

UNIVERSAL

RECIPIENT

(*YES is the preferred donor because the blood does contain other agglutinogens not listed here.)

The Rh Blood Group

The Rh factor was first studied in the rhesus monkey, thus the name Rh factor. It refers to several possible agglutinogens which may be found in the membrane of the red blood cells, primarily Agglutinogen D. Those who have these agglutinogens are considered to be Rh Positive (+), while those who do not are considered to be Rh Negative (-). As noted in the ABO Groupings, one would not transfuse blood to another that contains different agglutinogens. Technically, an Rh positive (+) person should not give blood to an Rh negative (-) person.

The distribution of the Rh blood groupings in the general population are represented by the following table.

Table L

Rh + (positive) 85 % of the Population has it

Rh - (negative) 15 % of the Population does NOT have it

Erythroblastosis fetalis

Erythroblastosis fetalis is a condition which can devlelop when a pregnant mother is Rh negative and the baby has Rh positive blood inherited from the father. The mother's body can develop antibodies against the Rh+ factor in the baby's blood if mixing of the two blood supplies occurs from a ruptured placenta during delivery. This does not have an effect on the child being born, but if the mother has subsequent pregnancies, these antibodies may cause destruction of the fetus' blood cells. Treatments for this condition include giving the mother a vaccine to prevent the blood incompatibility ahead of time. In some cases, a last resort procedure of blood transfusions while the child is still in the uterus may be attempted.

Cardiology

Cardiology refers to the study of the heart. The **heart** is a muscular pump which serves to pump blood to all parts of the body. *(See Fig. 41)* The heart is found in the region of the trunk of the body, above the diaphragm, called the thoracic cavity. It is located in the inferior portion of the space between the two lungs called the **mediastinum.**

The heart is made up of three layers of tissue. The outermost layer of the heart is a serous membrane called the **epicardium** or **visceral pericardium.** The middle layer of the heart is the muscle layer and is called the **myocardium.** The innermost layer, adjacent to the lumen of the heart, is an endothelial layer called the **endocardium.**

The heart is divided into four chambers. The heart and its chambers are always identified by their relative location in the body in the anatomical position. Remember that the position "right" or "left" always refers to the body's right or left, not the observer's.

The superior, or upper, chambers of the heart are always the receiving chambers for blood entering the heart, and are called the **atria** (plural) or **atrium** (singular). They are identified as the **right atrium** and **left atrium**. The lower chambers of the heart always serve as the exit chambers for blood leaving the heart, and are called the **ventricles.** They are identified as the **right ventricle** and **left ventricle.**

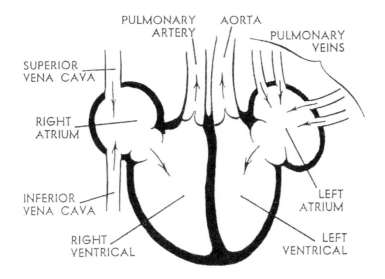

Chambers of the Heart

67

The dual pumping action of the heart produces two systems of circulation. One system is called **pulmonary circulation**. Pulmonary circulation refers to the blood vascular system which carries blood from the heart to the lungs for oxygenation and back to the heart. Because of this, the right ventricle of the heart is said to be the beginning of pulmonary circulation, and the left atrium is the end of pulmonary circulation.

Systemic circulation is the other part of the blood vascular system. It provides for blood circulation to all parts of the body, carrying nutrients and oxygenated blood, then returning back to the heart. This is the most extensive part of the blood circulatory system. Because of this, the left ventricle of the heart is said to be the beginning of systemic circulation, and the right atrium is the end of systemic circulation.

Each chamber of the heart has one or more vessels associated with it. Because the atria will serve as receiving chambers, the vessels which enter each atrium are always veins. Remember, a **vein** is a blood vessel which carries blood towards the heart. On the other hand, the ventricles are the exit chambers of the heart, and as such the vessel associated with each ventricle is called an artery. An **artery** is a blood vessel which will carry blood away from the heart.

The right atrium of the heart has three vessels which will enter the chamber. *(See Fig. 42)* The **superior vena cava** serves to drain the head, upper extremities, and part of the chest. The **inferior vena cava** provides the blood drainage from the abdomen and the lower extremities. The third vessel entering the right atrium is the **coronary sinus,** which drains the heart muscle itself and is not depicted since it enters from the back side.

The right ventricle of the heart has only one large vessel which exits the chamber, called the **pulmonary trunk,** or the **common pulmonary artery**. *(See Fig. 42)* It will carry the blood toward the lungs for oxygenation.

The left atrium of the heart has four vessels which will enter the chamber. These are the four **pulmonary veins.** *(See Fig. 42)* There are two of these vessels coming from each lung. They serve to return blood from the lungs which was delivered there for oxygenation by the pulmonary arteries.

The left ventricle of the heart has only one large vessel which exits the chamber. This vessel is called the **aorta,** or more specifically, the **ascending aorta**. It will carry the blood towards all parts of the body as part of systemic circulation.

The right and left atria are divided by a wall called the **atrial septum**, while the right and left ventricles are divided by a wall called the **ventricular septum**. The right atrium is separated from the right ventricle by a wall called the **right atrio-ventricular septum**, and the left atrium is separated from the left ventricle by the **left atrio-ventricular septum**.

In the right atrio-ventricular septum of the heart is a valve called the **tricuspid** or **right atrio-ventricular valve.** *(See Fig. 42)* The name tricuspid describes the fact that this valve is divided into three sections called cusps. The valve is designed much like a series of three small parachutes. The dome of the parachute is the cusp, the cords connecting the cusps are the **chordae tendineae**, and the man at the bottom of the cords is the **papillary muscle**. When the heart contracts, the cusps would billow and close the opening. The chordae tendineae prevent the inversion of the cusps and the papillary muscles are what hold the chordae tendineae in place.

In the left atrio-ventricular septum of the heart is a valve called the **bicuspid, mitral,** or **left atrio-ventricular valve**. *(See Fig. 42)* This valve is constructed slightly different from the tricuspid valve, but works essentially the same, and also has chordae tendineae attaching it to papillary muscles.

There are also valves located at the openings for the vessels which exit the heart. The valve at the exit of the right ventricle and the mouth of the pulmonary trunk is called the **pulmonary semilunar valve**. *(See Fig. 42)* The valve is comprised of three cusps that are like pockets on a shirt. They will allow the blood to flow away from the heart but they will billow and prevent the flow of blood back into the heart. When filled with blood each cusp resembles a half moon, consequently the name "semilunar".

The valve at the exit of the left ventricle into the mouth of the ascending aorta is called the **aortic semilunar valve**. *(See Fig. 42)* This valve's construction and function are identical to that of the pulmonary semilunar valve.

As noted earlier the heart is a muscle which pumps blood. It does so through a process called the **cardiac cycle**. The cycle involves two main stages referred to as systole and diastole.

The contraction phase of the cardiac cycle is called **systole.** It begins with the impulse to contract emitted by the **sino-atrial node** (or **SA-Node**), sometimes called the **pacemaker.** It is located in the back wall of the right atrium. The stimulus to contract then radiates through the heart muscle in all directions. Because of this, the two atria are the first to contract.

This contraction wave continues until it strikes another node called the **atrio-ventricular node** (or **AV-Node**). It is located, as its name implies, in the wall between the right atrium and right ventricle, adjacent to the opening of the tricuspid valve. The AV-Node is then responsible for picking up the signal to contract and sending the impulse to contract down through the walls of the ventricles. The two ventricles then contract after the atria have contracted.

Following systole, or the contraction phase of the cardiac cycle, the heart begins to relax, causing the chambers to expand or dilate. This is called **diastole,** or the dilation phase of the cardiac cycle. It proceeds in the same sequence as systole, beginning with the atria and followed by the ventricles.

Some experts like to discuss a third aspect of the heart cycle, and refer to it as the period of rest. However, it is not a totally separate period from systole and diastole, but merely the time frame during a cycle when both the atria and ventricles are in diastole at the same time. Thus, it could be said that the period of rest overlaps atrial and ventricular diastole.

In summary, let's trace the flow of blood through the heart beginning at the right atrium and ending by exiting the left ventricle.

Blood would enter the right atrium of heart through one of its three vessels: the superior vena cava, inferior vena cava, or the coronary sinus. It would then pass through the tricuspid or right atrio-ventricular valve into the right ventricle. Blood would then leave the heart, passing through the pulmonary semilunar valve into the pulmonary trunk or common pulmonary artery. This vessel then bifurcates into the right and left pulmonary arteries going to the lungs. While passing through the lungs, the blood is re-oxygenated, and then returns to the left atrium of the heart by way of the four pulmonary veins. From the left atrium, the blood must then pass through the mitral, bicuspid, or left atrio-ventricular valve into the left ventricle. The blood then passes through the aortic semilunar valve into the ascending aorta.

THE BLOOD VASCULAR SYSTEM
Chapter 10

Angiology

The study of the vessels of the body is called **angiology.** The blood vascular system is divided into two major types of vessels: the arteries and the veins. *(See Fig. 44 & 50)* The **arteries** will carry blood in the direction away from the heart, while **veins** will carry blood in the general direction towards the heart.

Arteries and veins are both composed of three general layers of tissue. *(See Fig. 43)* The inner-most layer is called the **tunica (layer) intima** or **interna.** This layer, also called the **endothelium,** is continuous with the endocardium of the heart. The endothelial layer can get its necessary blood supply directly from the blood as it passes through its lumen. The middle layer is called the **tunica media**. The tunica media is composed mainly of smooth muscle, which has the ability to contract and expand, allowing various amounts of blood through the arteries depending on bodily needs. The outer-most layer is called the **tunica adventitia** or **externa.** Due to the fact that substances such as oxygen and nutrients cannot pass through the multiple layers of vessels, the outer layers must get their oxygen and nutrients from another source. These layers, the tunica externa and media, receive their nourishment through tiny branches of other arteries. Collectively, these vessels which supply the outer layers of other vessels are called **vasa vasorum**, from the Latin meaning "vessels for vessels".

Very small arteries called **arterioles,** and very small veins called **venules,** will only have two layers in their walls. They will only have a tunica intima (or interna) and a tunica media. An arteriole results when an artery becomes so small that the outer layer disappears.

The smallest of the vessels are called **capillaries.** They have only one layer in their wall, called the tunica intima or interna. These are the vessels that will serve as the junction between the distal end of an artery and a vein. It is through the wall of the capillaries that we find the exchange of oxygen and carbon dioxide, plus the exchange of nutrients and wastes, between the cells of the body and the blood. After passing through the capillaries, blood begins its journey back towards the heart.

Not to be confused with the capillaries is the term anastomosis. Anastomosis refers to the union of the distal ends of two arteries. This may occur in places throughout the body where it is imperative that a blood supply be readily available to the particular body structure, even in cases where blockages may have occurred. Anastomoses are very commonly associated with the stomach and the intestinal tract. The brain and hands also exhibit prominent anastomoses.

Collateral circulation is another term which is often used in conjunction with anastomoses. Collateral circulation refers to two or more vessels providing blood supply to the same body part. We will learn later that the brain has four major vessels which provide it with a blood supply and the hands each have two major vessels.

Arteriology

By definition an artery is a vessel that carries blood away from the heart. Therefore, the vessels which begin in the ventricles of the heart are said to be arteries. The largest of these is the **aorta,** which begins in the left ventricle of the heart. It is customary to use the terminology of a tree when describing the arteries of the body. We will use words like **trunk** and **branches** to describe arteries since they tend to be much larger as they exit the heart and progressively get smaller as they branch out to all parts of the body.

The **aorta** begins at the **left ventricle** of the heart and ends at the bifurcation (splits into two) of the inferior end of the abdominal aorta where it becomes the **right and left common iliac arteries**.

The aorta is divided into four (4) sections. *(See Fig. 45)* The first section is the **ascending aorta**, the second is the **arch of the aorta**, the third is the **descending thoracic aorta**, and the fourth section is called the **abdominal aorta**. Each segment is named according to either its direction of flow and/or its location. Note that first three sections are all found in the thoracic cavity, so they are usually named according to the direction of flow. The third section, which is called the descending thoracic aorta, is not called just the "descending aorta", since the fourth section would also be considered to be descending. The last (fourth) section is simply referred to as the abdominal aorta because it is the only section located in the abdominal region.

Branches of the Aorta

The ascending aorta has only two branches. These branches are the **right and left coronary arteries,** which provide the blood supply to the myocardium, or heart muscle. They arise from the ascending aorta just beyond the aortic valve.

The **arch of the aorta** has three branches (which should be learned in order) identified as follows: (1) **brachiocephalic trunk** (or **innominate artery**), providing the blood supply to the right upper extremity and right side of head and neck; (2) **left common carotid artery**, providing the blood supply to left side of head and neck; and (3) **left subclavian artery**, providing the blood supply to left upper extremity. *(See Fig. 41 & 42)*

The **descending thoracic aorta** has two general types of branches. Those that provide the blood supply to the walls surrounding the cavities are called **parietal branches** and those providing the blood supply to the organs contained within the cavity are called **visceral branches.**

The **parietal branches** of the descending thoracic aorta are of three kinds: (1) **posterior intercostal arteries** (9 pairs), which provide the blood supply to the rib spaces 3-11; (2) **subcostal arteries** (1 pair), which provide the blood supply to the area below the last ribs; and (3) **superior phrenic arteries** (1 pair), which provide the blood supply to the top side of the diaphragm (phrenic muscle).

The visceral branches of the descending thoracic aorta are of three groups: (1) **esophageal arteries** (several pairs), which provide the blood supply to the esophagus; (2) **bronchial arteries** (several pairs), which provide the blood supply to the bronchi and the lungs; and (3) **pericardial arteries** (several pairs), which provide the blood supply to the pericardial sac (NOT the heart itself).

The abdominal aorta also has parietal and visceral branches. The major distinction is that it has visceral branches divided into those that are paired visceral and those that are unpaired visceral branches.

The parietal branches of the abdominal aorta are of three groups: *(See Fig. 45)* (1) **inferior phrenic arteries** (1 pair), which provide the blood supply to the underside of diaphragm; (2) **lumbar arteries** (4 pairs), which provide the blood supply to the small of the back; and (3) **mid-sacral artery** (unpaired), which provides the blood supply to the area near the tailbone.

The **paired visceral branches** of the abdominal aorta are of three groups: *(See Fig. 45)* (1) **suprarenal (or adrenal) arteries** (1 pair), which provide the blood supply to the suprarenal (or adrenal) glands; (2) **renal arteries** (1 pair), which provide the blood supply to the kidneys; and (3) **gonadal** (or **ovarian or testicular**) **arteries** (1 pair), which provide the blood supply to the sex glands.

These are the **unpaired visceral branches** of the abdominal aorta: *(See Fig. 45)* (1) **celiac trunk** (or **celiac axis or celiac artery**), which provides the blood supply to the stomach, liver, gall bladder, spleen, pancreas, and part of the small intestine (duodenum) by way of either the **left gastric artery, splenic artery, or common hepatic arteries**; (2) **superior mesenteric artery**, which provides the blood supply to the remainder of the small intestine (jejunum and ileum) and the first half of the large intestine (caecum, ascending colon, and transverse colon) by way of either the **intestinal branches, ileocolic artery, right colic, or middle colic arteries**; and (3) **inferior mesenteric artery** which provides the blood supply to the terminal portion (or the last half) of the large intestine (i.e. the descending colon, sigmoid colon, rectum, and anus) by way of either the **left colic artery, sigmoid artery**, or the **superior rectal arteries**.

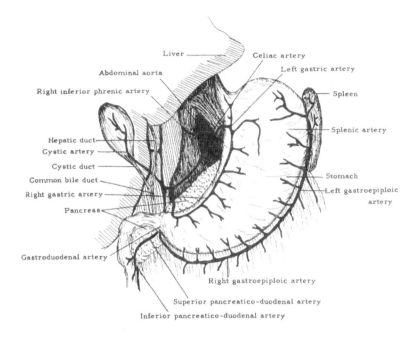

Celiac Trunk Arteries

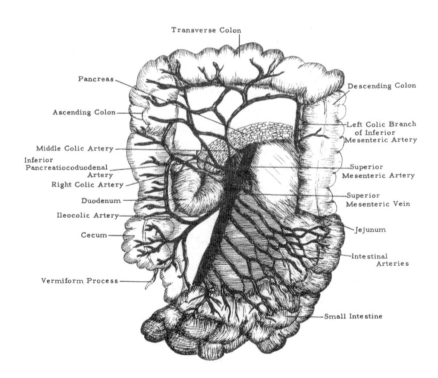

Superior Mesenteric Arteries

74

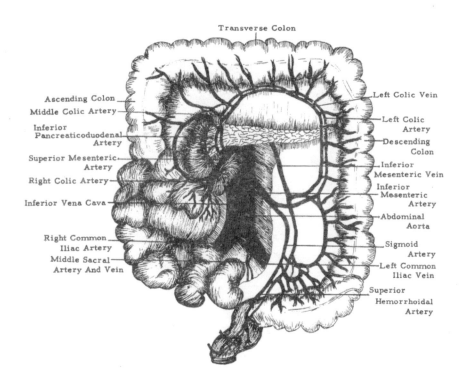

Transverse Colon

Ascending Colon

Middle Colic Artery

Inferior Pancreaticoduodenal Artery

Superior Mesenteric Artery

Right Colic Artery

Inferior Vena Cava

Right Common Iliac Artery

Middle Sacral Artery And Vein

Left Colic Vein

Left Colic Artery

Descending Colon

Inferior Mesenteric Vein

Inferior Mesenteric Artery

Abdominal Aorta

Sigmoid Artery

Left Common Iliac Vein

Superior Hemorrhoidal Artery

Inferior Mesenteric Arteries

Arteries of the Lower Extremity

As previously mentioned, the **aorta** ends where it bifurcates into the **right and left common iliac arteries**. *(See Fig. 45)* The common iliac arteries lie just above the top of the psoas major muscles of the abdomen, along a line running towards the center of the inguinal ligament. The common iliac arteries also bifurcate, giving rise to both the **internal iliac artery** (or **hypogastric artery**) and the **external iliac artery**. *(See Fig. 46)*

The internal iliac arteries are the vessels which provide the blood supply to the gluteal region, the urinary bladder, and the uterus in the female body, as well as give rise to the **umbilical arteries** during fetal circulation.

The external iliac arteries serve as the continuation of the common iliac arteries and continue along the medial border of the psoas muscles toward the lower extremities. When the external iliac artery passes under the inguinal ligament its name changes, and it becomes known as the **femoral artery**. *(See Fig. 46)*

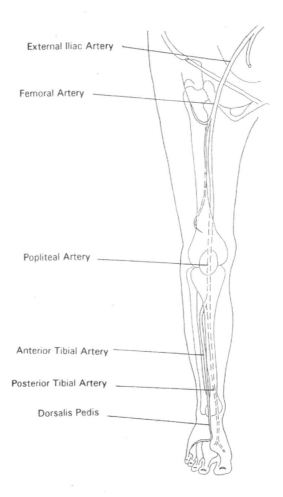

External Iliac Artery

Femoral Artery

Popliteal Artery

Anterior Tibial Artery

Posterior Tibial Artery

Dorsalis Pedis

Arteries of the Lower Extremity

The femoral artery gives rise to several branches as it descends through the region of the thigh before passing through the opening of the adductor magnus muscle, where it becomes the **popliteal artery**. *(See Fig. 46)* Among its branches are the **medial and lateral femoral circumflex arteries**, which provide the blood supply to the hip joint as well as the muscles of the superior-most portion of the thigh. The other branch of the femoral artery is the **deep femoral** (or **femoral profundus**) **artery.** It runs much deeper and parallel to the femoral artery providing the blood supply to the bone and muscles of the thigh.

The popliteal artery is the continuation of the femoral artery as it passes through the opening in the adductor magnus muscle, at which point it lies behind the inferior-most portion of the femur. The popliteal runs directly behind the knee in the popliteal space and gives off branches providing the blood supply to the knee joint. The branches of the popliteal artery are the **genicular** arteries (note "genu" means knee, as in genuflect, or to bend the knee). There are usually four (4) of these branches identified by their location, as in the **superior medial genicular artery** or **inferior lateral genicular artery.**

The popliteal artery extends to just below the bend of the knee where it bifurcates into the **anterior tibial artery** and the **posterior tibial artery**, which extend to the foot. *(See Fig. 46)*

The **anterior tibial artery** extends inferiorly along the anterior-lateral surface of the tibia (the shin), to the top of the foot where it becomes the **dorsalis pedis artery** (or the **great dorsal artery of the foot**). *(See Fig. 46)* The dorsalis pedis artery continues down onto the foot where it gives rise to a branch called the **arcuate artery**. Arising from the arcuate artery are branches to the toes called **digital arteries**. *(See Fig. 46)*

The **posterior tibial artery** gives rise to a branch as it descends through the leg called the **peroneal** (or **fibular**) **artery** which provides the blood supply to the muscles of the calf of the leg. *(See Fig. 46)* The continuation of the posterior tibial artery enters the foot behind the medial malleolus where it bifurcates into the **medial** and **lateral plantar arteries** of the foot. These then give rise to additional digital arteries providing the blood supply to the toes.

Arteries of the Upper Extremity

As noted earlier, the **arch of the aorta** has 3 branches, including the: (1) **brachiocephalic trunk (or innominate artery)**, providing the blood supply to the right upper extremity and right side of head and neck; (2) left **common carotid artery**, providing the blood supply to left side of head and neck; and (3) **left subclavian artery**, providing the blood supply to left upper extremity. *(See Fig. 41 & 42)*

A distinction should be noted in the manner in which blood from the arch of the aorta proceeds to each of the upper extremities. The **brachiocephalic trunk** is a relaitively short artery (1½ – 2") which terminates by bufurcating into the **right subclavian artery** and the **right common carotid artery**. The right subclavian artery is then very similar to the left subclavian artery in that each gives rise to similar branches and have similar points of termination, though their origins differ. The right common carotid artery also resembles the left common carotid artery in that it gives rise to similar branches and has a similar termination, both of which will be discussed later.

Each of the **subclavian arteries** extends laterally toward the corresponding upper extremity, changing names to become the **axillary artery** as it passes the lateral border of the first rib.

The subclavian arteries give rise to several major branches.

The **vertebral artery** is a branch of the subclavian artery which courses up the neck, passing through the transverse processes of most of the cervical vertebrae. It provides the blood supply to parts of the spinal cord and brain stem. The vertebral arteries end by passing through the floor of the cranium and then uniting to form the **basilar artery**, which feeds into the **Circle of Willis** (or **cerebral arterial circle**).

The **internal thoracic artery** (or **internal mammary artery**) is another branch of the subclavian artery. It descends along the anterior thoracic wall giving rise to the anterior intercostal arteries. Each runs just lateral to the sternum, providing the blood supply to the rib spaces. The anterior intercostal arteries will anastomose with the corresponding posterior intercostal artery, thereby providing a continuous blood supply to the rib spaces.

The other two branches of the subclavian artery are the **thyro-cervical trunk** and the **costo-cervical trunk**. The thyro-cervical trunk gives origin to branches which provide the blood supply to the underside of the thyroid gland, anterior root of the neck, and the area of the shoulder just above the scapula. The costo-cervical trunk's branches provide the blood supply to the posterior intercostal spaces # 1 and # 2 (refer to the parietal branches of the descending thoracic aorta for the other posterior intercostal arteries) as well as deep muscles of the neck.

As the subclavian artery passes the lateral border of the first rib it becomes the axillary artery. It should be noted that the axillary artery is very deep until it becomes superficial in the axillary space (the area under the arm, armpit). The axillary artery gives rise to branches providing the blood supply to the shoulder joint, muscles of the chest wall and of the shoulder, as well as around the head of the humerus.

The **axillary artery** extends into the arm to a point just inferior to the lower border of the tendon of the teres major muscle, where it becomes the **brachial artery**. *(See Fig. 47)* The brachial artery courses down through the arm to a point just inferior to the bend of the elbow where it bifurcates into its terminal branches, the **radial artery** and the **ulnar artery**.

The most prominent branch of the brachial artery is the **deep brachial** (or **brachial profundus**) **artery**, which runs parallel to the brachial artery providing the blood supply to the muscles of the arm. *(See Fig. 47)* Other branches provide the blood supply to muscles of the elbow joint.

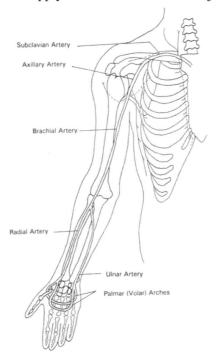

Subclavian Artery

Axillary Artery

Brachial Artery

Radial Artery

Ulnar Artery

Palmar (Volar) Arches

Arteries of the Upper Extremity

The forearm has two major arteries, the radial artery and the ulnar artery. Both are formed from the bifurcation of the brachial artery.

The radial artery lies on the lateral side of the forearm while the ulnar artery lies on the medial side, each parallel to the corresponding bone of similar name. Each vessel continues into the palm of the hand where it becomes one of the **palmar** (or **volar**) **arches**. *(See Fig. 47)* The radial artery becomes the deep palmar (or volar) arch which loops around and connects with the ulnar artery. The radial artery is relatively close to the anterior surface at the wrist which is why it is often used to take one's pulse. It is also one of the easiest vessels to raise in order to inject the hand during the embalming procedure, since it lies just lateral to the tendon of the flexor carpi radialis muscle.

The ulnar artery becomes the **superficial palmar** (or **volar**) **arch** which loops around and connects with the radial artery. *(See Fig. 47)* Branches of the palmar arches providing the blood supply to the fingers are called the **digital arteries**. Note that there are digital arteries in both the hands and feet.

Arteries of the Head and Neck

Remember that the arch of the aorta has 3 branches, two of which provide the blood supply to each side of the head and neck. They include the **brachiocephalic trunk (or innominate artery)**, providing the blood supply to the right upper extremity and right side of head and neck, and the **left common carotid artery** providing the blood supply to the left side of head and neck. The common carotid arteries are very similar in their branches and points of termination, though each differs in its point of origin.

The common carotid arteries extend up the neck to a point just below the level of the jaw-line where each bifurcates into the corresponding **internal carotid artery** and **external carotid artery**. *(See Fig. 25 & 48)* The external carotid artery provides the blood supply to structures of the neck and head which, in general, lie outside of the cranium. The internal carotid artery provides the blood supply to the brain (within the cranial cavity) and the eyes.

The **external carotid artery** has eight (8) branches serving the neck and outside of the skull. *(See Fig. 48)* The **superior thyroid artery** provides the blood supply to the superior portion of the thyroid gland. The **lingual artery** is the blood supply to the tongue. The **facial artery** provides the blood supply to most of the face. It has its own branches, the **mental artery** supplying the chin, the **superior and inferior labial arteries** supplying the lips, and the **nasal artery** supplying the area around the nose. The **occipital artery** provides the blood supply to the scalp at the back of the skull. The **posterior auricular artery** provides the blood supply to the area of scalp directly behind each ear. The **ascending pharyngeal artery** provides the blood supply to the pharynx (the throat area directly behind the mouth). The **maxillary artery** provides the blood supply to the bones of the jaw and roof of the mouth. The **superficial temporal artery**, which is the terminal continuation of the external carotid artery, provides the blood supply to the region of the scalp just anterior to the ears.

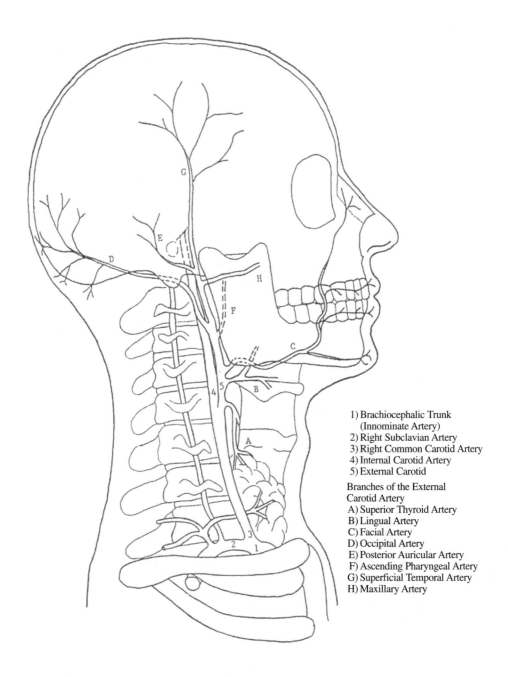

1) Brachiocephalic Trunk
   (Innominate Artery)
2) Right Subclavian Artery
3) Right Common Carotid Artery
4) Internal Carotid Artery
5) External Carotid

Branches of the External
Carotid Artery
A) Superior Thyroid Artery
B) Lingual Artery
C) Facial Artery
D) Occipital Artery
E) Posterior Auricular Artery
F) Ascending Pharyngeal Artery
G) Superficial Temporal Artery
H) Maxillary Artery

Arteries of the Head and Neck

The **internal carotid artery** is the branch of the common carotid artery which provides the blood supply to those areas of the head which are located primarily inside of the cranial cavity, and to the eyes. *(See Fig. 49)* There are four major branches of the internal carotid artery. The **ophthalmic artery** is the branch which provides the blood supply to the eye. The other three branches are all closely related to the blood supply of the brain. The **anterior cerebral artery** and the **posterior communicating artery** are branches which are part of the **Circle of Willis** (or the **cerebral arterial circle**). The **middle cerebral artery** is the fourth branch and, along with the anterior cerebral, is a terminal branch of the internal carotid artery providing the blood supply up the side of the brain.

The **cerebral arterial circle** (or the **Circle of Willis**) is where the arteries providing the blood supply to the brain anastomose, providing multiple sources of blood supply to this vital organ. *(See Fig. 49)*There are four major arteries which direct blood toward the brain. They are the **right and left internal carotid arteries** and the **right and left vertebral arteries**. The two vertebral arteries unite after they enter the cranial cavity to become the **basilar artery**. The basilar artery then feeds into the Circle of Willis by bifurcating into the **right and left posterior cerebral arteries**.

The **Circle of Willis** is generally considered to be made up of nine (9) arteries. They are the **right and left internal carotid arteries**, the **anterior communicating artery**, which serves to link the **right and left anterior cerebral arteries**, the **right and left posterior cerebral arteries**, and the **right and left posterior communicating arteries** which link the internal carotid artery to the corresponding posterior cerebral artery. Some may include the **basilar artery** as part of the Circle if Willis. If this is done there would be ten arteries in the make-up of the cerebral arterial circle.

Phlebology

Phlebology refers to the study of the veins of the body. *(See Fig. 50)* Remember that a **vein** carries blood toward the heart. Veins, unlike the arteries, may have valves within their lumen. This is true for most veins found below the level of the heart. Exceptions to this are those veins which enter the heart and those found in the hepatic portal system. Many of the veins tend to be much larger than the adjacent arteries because they contain blood that is moving much slower. As with arteries, veins will have three layers in their walls, with the main difference being in the thickness of the layers; in veins these layers are much thinner. The names of the layers are the same for veins as they were for arteries: tunica interna (intima), tunica media, and tunica externa (adventitia).

As we discuss the venous system, we will use terminology relating to rivers and streams. Since veins tend to merge to form larger veins as they approach the heart, we will describe them as **tributaries** to other veins. Note that when we are talking about a vein which has the same name as the accompanying artery, their anatomical limits will be reversed due to the opposite direction of their blood flow.

Veins are usually divided into two groups, including those that are said to be part of the **deep set** and those that are part of the **superficial set** of veins. The **deep set** of veins includes those that generally accompany the arterial system. They usually lie side by side with an artery, often carrying the same name as the artery. As the name implies, they are generally deep in the body. In many areas of our body, particularly the extremities, there are often two small veins accompanying an artery of the same name. Collectively, these double veins which accompany an artery are referred to as **venae commitantes** (companion veins).

The **superficial set** of veins includes a group of veins which are generally located near the surface of the body. They do not accompany any particular artery, nor do they carry the same name as any artery. We will limit our discussion of superficial veins to those in the upper and lower extremities.

Veins of the Thoracic Region

We have previously discussed the manner of termination of the veins entering the heart, but must also mention their origins. *(See Fig. 51)* The superior vena cava is formed by the union of the **right and left brachiocephalic (innominate) veins.** The **brachiocephalic veins** are formed by the union of the **internal jugular vein** and the corresponding **subclavian vein.** The **inferior vena cava** is formed by the union of the **right and left common iliac veins**. The coronary sinus results from the uniting of the small coronary veins coming from the heart muscle. The **pulmonary veins** result from the merging of many small veins coming from the capillary beds in the lungs.

The **azygos system** is a group of veins which serve to drain blood from the walls and organs of the thoracic cavity. *(See Fig. 51)* It is comprised of the azygos vein, hemiazygos vein, accessory hemiazygos vein, and their tributaries. The **azygos vein** begins as a continuation of the right ascending lumbar vein at about the level of the right kidney, and courses up through the diaphragm, draining the intercostal veins on the right side. It terminates by emptying into the superior vena cava.

The **hemiazygos vein** begins as a continuation of the left ascending lumbar vein at about the level of the left kidney, courses up through the diaphragm, and drains the intercostal veins on the left side. It terminates by crossing over, at about the level of the heart, and emptying into the azygos vein. The **accessory hemiazygos vein** begins as a continuation of one of the first intercostal veins on the left side and descends along the vertebral column to about the level of the heart, where it empties into the hemiazygos vein.

Veins of the Abdominal Region

The tributaries to the inferior vena cava are in some respects not unlike the branches of the abdominal aorta. The tributaries can be divided into parietal or visceral tributaries.

Parietal tributaries would be those veins that are draining the walls surrounding the cavity, while those that are visceral tributaries would serve to drain the organs. The **parietal tributaries** of the inferior vena cava include the **lumbar veins**, which drain the walls of the lower back, and the **inferior phrenic veins**, which drain the underside of the diaphragm.

The **visceral tributaries** of the inferior vena cava include the **hepatic veins**, which drain the hepatic portal system; the **right and left renal veins**, which drain the kidneys and left-side paired organs; **right gonadal (or ovarian or testicular) vein**, which drains the right ovary or testicle; and the **right suprarenal (or adrenal) vein**, which drains the right suprarenal or adrenal gland. *(See Fig. 52)*

Anatomically, the **inferior vena cava** lies on the right side of the abdominal aorta. Therefore, for the veins to empty into it from the left side they must cross over the aorta. Because of this, the **left suprarenal (or adrenal) vein** empties not into the inferior vena cava, but instead into the **left renal vein,** which is a tributary to the inferior vena cava. Similarly, the **left gonadal (or ovarian or testicular) vein** empties into the **left renal vein,** which then empties into the inferior vena cava. *(See Fig. 52)*

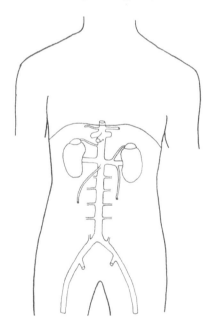

Abdominal Veins

The **hepatic portal system** is the system of veins which serve to drain the organs of digestion in the abdomen. The blood from these organs must first pass through the liver. This accomplishes several functions. One function is to filter the blood by removing various substances. Some of these substances, such as glucose, are modified and stored by the liver, while harmful substances absorbed from the digestive tract are detoxified and eventually eliminated from the body by the kidneys.

83

The **hepatic portal system** includes the **inferior mesenteric vein** and its tributaries, which drain the last half of the large intestine. The **inferior mesenteric vein** is itself a tributary to the **splenic vein**, which has tributaries from the pancreas, spleen, and stomach. The **superior mesenteric vein** is also part of the portal system, and has tributaries which come from the small intestine and the first half of the large intestine. The **splenic vein** and the **superior mesenteric vein** then unite to form the **portal vein,** which bifurcates as it enters the liver. After being filtered in the liver, the blood is then drained by way of the several **hepatic veins,** which are tributaries to the **inferior vena cava**.

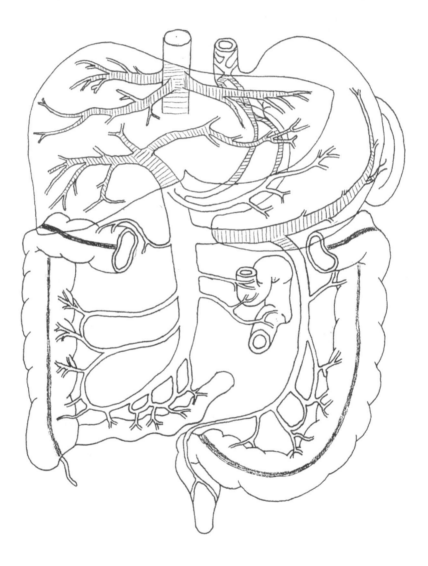

Hepatic Portal System

Veins of the Head and Neck Region

The **dural sinuses** are veins which drain the brain. They serve to drain the structures inside of the cranial cavity. They derive their names from the dura mater, the outer membrane surrounding the brain and spinal cord. They eventually empty into the **sigmoid sinus,** which gives rise to the **internal jugular vein**. The internal jugular vein then unites with the corresponding **subclavian vein** to form the **brachiocephalic vein**.

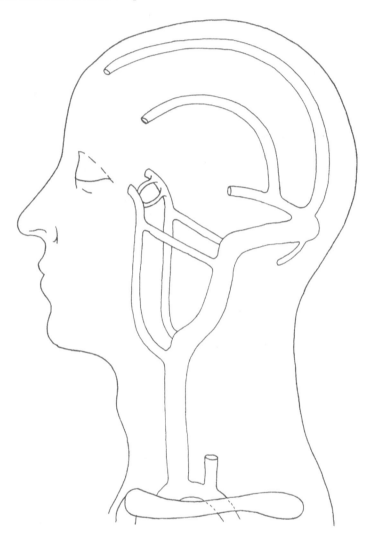

Dural Sinuses (Not to Scale)

Most of the veins draining the face and scalp have names similar to their corresponding arteries. *(Fig. 53)* Those veins of the face and scalp anterior to the ears empty into the **internal jugular vein**. The internal jugular vein is very important to many embalmers because it serves to drain both the brain and the face. Those veins which drain the scalp behind the ear are drained by the **external jugular vein**. The external jugular vein is, in turn, a tributary to the corresponding **subclavian vein**, before the subclavian unites with the internal jugular to form the brachiocephalic vein.

85

Veins of the Upper Extremity

The deep set of veins in the upper extremity have exactly the same name as the accompanying arteries. *(See Fig. 54)* Beginning in the forearm are the **radial veins** and the **ulnar veins**, which unite to form the **brachial vein** just below the bend of the elbow. The brachial vein courses up the extremity, and when it passes the tendon of the teres major muscle, it helps form the **axillary vein**. The **axillary vein** then becomes the **subclavian vein** as it passes the first rib. The **subclavian vein** unites with the **internal jugular vein** to become the **brachiocephalic vein**, which then unites with the opposite **brachiocephalic** (or **innominate**) **vein** to form the **superior vena cava.** *(See Fig. 51)*

The **superficial veins** of the upper extremity are the cephalic and basilic veins. *(See Fig. 54)* The **cephalic vein** begins on the lateral side of the hand and courses up the extremity to empty into the superior portion of the **axillary vein**. The **basilic vein** begins on the medial side of the hand and courses up the extremity, uniting with the **brachial vein** to become the **axillary vein**. The are various smaller veins which connect between the basilic and the cephalic veins, the most common one being the **median cubital vein**, often used by phebotomists from which to draw blood.

Veins of the Lower Extremity

As in the upper extremity, the **deep set** of veins in the lower extremity have the same names as their accompanying arteries. *(See Fig. 55)* Beginning at the lower portion of the leg, the **anterior tibial vein** unites with the **posterior tibial vein** to become the **popliteal vein** just below the bend of the knee. The **posterior tibial vein** has as a tributary the **peroneal vein** which drains the muscles of the calf.

The **popliteal vein** has as its tributaries the **genicular veins**, which help drain blood from the knee area, and then becomes the **femoral vein** as it passes through an opening in the adductor magnus muscle. The **femoral vein** courses up the thigh and passes under the inguinal ligament to become the **external iliac vein**. The **external iliac vein** then unites with the **internal iliac (or hypogastric) vein** to become the **common iliac vein**. The **right and left common iliac veins** then unite to form the **inferior vena cava.**

The **superficial veins** of the lower extremity are the two saphenous veins. The **long** (or **great**) **saphenous vein** begins on the medial side of the foot and courses up the extremity where it empties into the **femoral vein** in the region of the femoral triangle. This vein is perceptible in most people, particularly when it becomes varicosed following the deterioration of its valves. The **short** (or **lesser**) **saphenous vein** begins on the lateral side of the foot and courses up the extremity where it empties into the **popliteal vein**. Often times there will be interconnections with the greater saphenous vein.

THE LYMPHATIC SYSTEM
Chapter 11

The **lymphatic system** is generally not considered to be a separate system of the body, but rather a part of the circulatory system. Its connection with the circulatory system comes from the source of lymph. Lymph is derived from tissue fluid which, in turn, came from plasma that escaped the blood vascular system.

The lymphatic system is an extensive network of small vessels called **lymphatics,** whose purpose is to collect excess tissue fluid and return it to the blood vascular system by emptying into the veins. Unlike the blood vascular system, the lymphatics have no pumping mechanism. The contents of these vessels are transported by gravity and by the pressure of the surrounding structures compressing the vessels, such as muscular contractions.

Blood plasma which escapes through the walls of the capillaries, minus some of its essential proteins, becomes known as **tissue fluid**. Tissue fluid provides the important fluid environment in which body cells exist. It also serves as the transportation medium by which the cells of the body receive many nutrients and exchange respiratory gases and waste products. Much of the tissue fluid eventually re-enters the bloodstream through the capillary walls, but that which does not is picked up by special lymphatic vessels. The tissue fluid which enters these lymphatic vessels is now referred to as **lymph.** Thus we can see the intimate relationship between these important body fluids. Plasma is the liquid portion of blood; much of it becomes tissue fluid outside of the vessels, and the tissue fluid which enters the lymphatic vessels is known as lymph. This lymph is eventually emptied back into the bloodstream and again becomes blood plasma. Occasionally tissue fluid builds up in excess and is not carried away by the capillaries or the lymphatic vessels. When this occurs it is referred to as **edema,** which can lead to a swelling and distention of the tissues.

Characteristics of Lymph

Lymph is a pale amber-colored liquid that is odorless, has a salty taste, a specific gravity of 1.015, and is **slightly alkaline with a pH of 7.4**. It moves very slowly due only to gravity and pressure from surrounding structures (mostly muscle movements).

Vessels of the lymphatic system

Similar to the veins, lymphatics have three (3) layers in their walls (intima, media, adventitia) and valves to keep the lymph moving toward the heart. The **right lymphatic duct** serves to drain lymph from the **superior right quadrant** of the body. *(See Fig. 56)* This vessel is formed from the small lymph vessels draining this area. It is a relatively small vessel which empties into one of the veins of the neck, generally the right subclavian or right brachiocephalic vein.

The **left lymphatic duct** (or the **thoracic duct**) serves to drain lymph from the **superior left quadrant and both inferior quadrants of the body**. *(See Fig. 56)* The **thoracic duct** begins at the **cisterna chyli** in the abdomen and courses up the thoracic cavity, where it empties into the left subclavian or left brachiocephalic vein on the left side of the neck.

The **cisterna chyli** is the dilated (enlarged) inferior end of the thoracic duct, which is the collecting place for lymph coming from the abdomen and the lower extremities. *(See Fig. 56)*

The small lymph vessels which drain the lymph from the digestive tract, specifically from the ileum of the small intestine, are called **lacteals.** The name **lacteal** comes from the milky-like appearance of the lymph found in these vessels. This is due to the presence of fats that are dissolved in the lymph. This special kind of lymph is called **chyle.**

There are prominent clusters of **lymph nodes** located in various areas of the body. One of these clusters found embedded in the walls of the small intestine and is referred to as **Peyer's Patches**. This group of lymph nodes helps to filter lymph leaving the intestinal area via the lacteals. Major clusters of lymph nodes are also found located in the axilla, groin, breast area, neck, and along the major vessels of the body.

Certain types of malignancies are known to spread (**metastasize**) by way of the lymph vessels, including Hodgkin's Disease (which involves the cervical lymph nodes) and breast cancer.

Tonsils are masses of lymphoid tissue found embedded in the walls of the throat, and the **thymus gland** is a significant mass of lymphoid tissue located behind the top of the sternum. The thymus gland is important to the body's immune system, as it is involved in the early development of many lymphocytes. Lymphocytes are blood cells responsible for assisting in the protection of the body against various infectious diseases.

The largest mass of lymphoid tissue in the body is the **spleen,** which is located in the left hypochondriac region of the abdominal cavity. The spleen is important in phagocytosis of many bacterial and other foreign particles, including worn out blood cells which the body no longer needs. In addition, the spleen serves as a reservoir for extra red blood cells which might be needed on short notice by the body.

THE ENDOCRINE SYSTEM
Chapter 12

The prefix "adeno" comes from the Greek word meaning gland, so adenology refers to the study of glands. A gland is a body organ which gives off a secretion to be used elsewhere in the body. The glands in the human body are generally categorized based on where the secretions they produce are delivered. Glands which give off internal secretions that are absorbed directly into the bloodstream for distribution all over the body are called endocrine (endo=inside) glands. Endocrine glands are sometimes referred to as "ductless" glands, as their secretions are carried off by the bloodstream, and do not need to pass through a duct of any sort. This group of glands, which will be the focus of this chapter, is generally considered to be a separate bodily system. *(See Fig. 57)*

There also exist in the human body a number of glands whose secretions are not absorbed directly into the bloodstream, but are delivered outside of the gland, via a duct, to a specific body area. Glands which function in this manner are referred to as exocrine (exo=outside) glands. Examples of **exocrine** glands would include sweat and oil glands in the skin, and salivary glands which deliver saliva into the mouth. These glands are not usually discussed as a separate body system, but in conjunction with the main system where their secretions are put to use. For instance, the oil and sweat glands will be discussed with the integumentary system, and the salivary glands with the digestive system. Some glands in the body produce both endocrine and exocrine secretions, in which case they are referred to as **heterocrine** glands.

The endocrine system, along with the nervous system, is one of the main controlling systems in the human body. The chemical secretions given off by endocrine glands, which are called **hormones,** are delivered all over the body by the bloodstream, and chemically stimulate changes in the metabolic activities of various cells in the body. The term hormone comes from the Greek word meaning to arouse, or set in motion. Hormones function by setting in motion various physiological activities within the cells of the organs upon which they act. Although hormones are carried by the blood all over the body, many tend to be specific in nature, meaning they only stimulate activity within the cells of certain organs. These organs in turn would be referred to as the "target" organs for that particular hormone.

The Pituitary Gland

The **pituitary gland,** also known as the hypophysis cerebri, is a small but extremely important gland, located on the under surface of the brain, where it is attached to that part of the brain called the hypothalamus. *(See Fig. 57 & 59)* The pituitary is situated within the depression in the sphenoid bone called the sella turcica. Because the pituitary gland regulates so many bodily functions, and stimulates other endocrine glands to perform their functions, it is often referred to as the **master gland.**

Anatomically, the pituitary gland is composed of an anterior and a posterior lobe. The anterior lobe is the main endocrine portion of the pituitary, producing several important hormones for distribution throughout the body. One of these hormones is called somatotrophic hormone (STH), or simply the **growth hormone.** It is called the growth hormone because it is responsible for the rate at which amino acids enter the cells of the body and are built up into proteins, thus promoting normal growth of the tissues. As you can imagine, abnormal amounts of this growth hormone can have dramatic effects on an individual's development. For instance, too much of this growth hormone in a developing child can lead to an abnormally large person, a condition referred to as pituitary giantism. On the contrary, too little growth hormone in a child may lead to the opposite effect of pituitary dwarfism. Other abnormalities may result if over or under secretion of growth hormone occurs after normal growth has occurred and ossification has taken place. Following is a list of other hormones elaborated by the anterior pituitary, and their basic functions:

TABLE

1. follicle stimulating hormone (FSH) - stimulates the ovaries of the female to develop an ovum each month and to produce estrogen, a female sex hormone. In males it stimulates sperm and sex hormone production by the testes.

2. luteinizing hormone (LH) - works with FSH to stimulate ovulation and sex hormones in females, and the production of testosterone, the male sex hormone.

3. prolactin - stimulates milk secretion by the mammary glands after pregnancy.

4. melanocyte stimulating hormone (MSH) - affects the production and distribution of melanin, a skin coloring pigment.

5. thyroid stimulating hormone (TSH) - stimulates the thyroid gland to produce its hormones.

6. adrenocorticotropic hormone (ACTH) - stimulates the adrenal glands to produce their hormones.

The posterior lobe of the pituitary is technically not an endocrine gland because it does not actually make hormones, but it does store some which were made by the hypothalamus of the brain, for release as needed in the body. One of these main hormones released by the posterior pituitary is called anti-diuretic hormone (ADH). This hormone has the effect of regulating urine output by the kidneys. It actually functions by allowing the kidneys to return much needed water into the bloodstream, thus decreasing the total volume of urine output. In the absence of ADH, the kidneys may eliminate far too much water through the urinary system, causing dangerous dehydration of the body.

The Thyroid Gland

The thyroid gland is located in the inferior, anterior cervical region, just below the voicebox. *(See Fig. 57)* It is made up of two lobes connected by a narrow central portion called the isthmus. Anatomically, it can be seen to wrap partially around the trachea, with the narrow isthmus situated on the midline.

The two main hormones secreted by the thyroid are called **thyroxin** and **calcitonin.** Thyroxin is an extremely important hormone, affecting all of the cells in the body. It functions to control the rate at which the cells of the body release energy from the nutrients which have been taken in. In other words, it directly affects cellular metabolism, sometimes expressed as the basal metabolic rate (BMR). In addition to its control over metabolism, thyroxin helps regulate growth of the tissues in the body, and has a stimulatory effect on the heart rate. As you can imagine, disturbances in the amount of thyroxin can have far reaching effects in the body, as this vital hormone is necessary for the proper day to day functioning of the cells of the body.

The other thyroid hormone, calcitonin, acts to decrease blood calcium levels by inhibiting the breakdown of bone cells which contain calcium. Thus, it can be said that calcitonin is important in maintaining homeostasis of calcium in the bloodstream. If an increase in blood calcium is detected, additional calcitonin is secreted by the thyroid in an effort to return the amount of blood calcium to normal levels.

The thyroid gland is somewhat unique, compared to other endocrine glands, in its ability to store excess quantities of its hormones. Whereas the secretions of most endocrine glands immediately enter the bloodstream for distribution around the body, the thyroid can keep in reserve those quantities of hormones not immediately needed by the cells of the body.

The Parathyroid Glands

The parathyroid glands are four in number, and are found embedded in the posterior surface of the thyroid. *(See Fig. 57)* Thus, their name is appropriate, as the prefix "para" means "about", or "in the vicinity of". The parathyroids secrete a hormone called **parathormone,** which is important in regulating blood calcium levels. It can be said that parathormone is antagonistic to calcitonin from the thyroid gland, as it acts to increase blood calcium levels. If blood calcium falls below a certain point, parathormone is released into the bloodstream, and stimulates bone cells to break down and release additional calcium. As you can see, proper levels of hormones from both the thyroid and the parathyroid are important in maintaining homeostasis in the body.

The Suprarenal (Adrenal) Glands

As the name **suprarenal** (supra=above, renal=kidney) suggests, these glands are situated one on top of each kidney. *(See Fig. 57)* They are composed of two main layers, an outer layer called the **cortex,** and an inner layer called the **medulla.** *(See Fig. 34)*

The adrenal cortex is subdivided into three layers, or zones, which produce a group of hormones called corticoids. The three zones of the cortex, and the hormones which they produce, are identified as follows:

1. zona glomerulosa - produces **mineralcorticoids,** which are important in maintaining proper levels of certain minerals in the bloodstream, particularly sodium and potassium. These hormones function by affecting the amount of these minerals which are given off by the kidneys through the urinary system.

2. zona fasciculata - secretes **glucocorticoids,** such as cortisone and hydrocortisone, which help to maintain proper levels of glucose in the blood. They increase blood glucose by stimulating the breakdown of carbohydrates into glucose, and by causing the liver to make additional glucose from amino acids. This is extremely important, as glucose serves as the main energy source for the cells of the body. In addition, glucocorticoids have the effect of maintaining proper blood pressure, and perform an anti-inflammatory function, which decreases blood vessel dilation and the resulting edema associated with various inflammations.

3. zona reticularis - secretes **gonadocorticoids,** which are actually weak sex hormones, similar to testosterone. They are normally produced in small amounts in both males and females, but abnormalities can occur which produce dramatic masculinizing effects, particularly in women.

The adrenal medulla secretes the hormone known as **adrenaline,** or **epinephrine.** Adrenaline is secreted into the bloodstream by the medulla in times of stress, and helps put the body into a "supercharged" state by increasing such functions as heart rate and blood pressure. This hormone has often been described as stimulating the body's "fight or flight" response to stress.

The Gonads

The female gonads, or **ovaries**, give off two main hormones, called **estrogen** and **progesterone.** *(See Fig. 36 & 57)* Estrogen is mainly responsible for development of female sexual characteristics, such as maturing of the sexual organs and breasts, and helps to regulate the menstrual cycle. Progesterone works in conjunction with estrogen in regulating the menstrual cycle, preparing the uterus for pregnancy, and stimulating the breasts to produce milk.

The male gonads, or **testes**, produce **testosterone** as their endocrine secretion. *(See Fig. 35 & 57)* Testosterone is responsible for the development of male sexual characteristics. It is often described as the masculinizing hormone, due to its role in causing such changes as the deepening of the voice at puberty, the production of male sex cells, or spermatozoa, and the growth of body hair.

In addition to these endocrine functions of both the female and male gonads, they each possess important exocrine functions as well. In the male, spermatozoa are produced which are given off into the spermatic duct, and in the female, ova are produced, which travel from the ovary to the uterus through the fallopian tubes. As a result, the male and female gonads are often described as heterocrine glands, because they perform both endocrine and exocrine functions.

The Pancreas

The pancreas is another example of a heterocrine gland, because it produces endocrine secretions, plus an exocrine secretion called **pancreatic juice.** *(See Fig. 29 & 57)* Pancreatic juice is a digestive enzyme which travels through the pancreatic duct to be eventually emptied into the small intestine for the digestion of fats.

Contained within the pancreas are specialized groups of cells called the **Islets of Langerhans**, which produce the two endocrine secretions called **glucagon** and **insulin.** Glucagon is a hormone which stimulates the liver to increase the rate at which glucose is released into the bloodstream. Insulin, on the other hand, can be described as being antagonistic to glucagon. This is because insulin has the effect of decreasing blood glucose levels by influencing the movement of glucose molecules out of the blood and into the individual cells of the body. Too much insulin in the blood can result in a serious decrease in vital blood glucose levels, and conversely, too little insulin can result in a build-up of blood glucose levels, and consequently the elimination of these excess amounts of glucose through the urinary system. These conditions of having excessive levels of glucose in the blood and the urine are common signs of the disease known as diabetes mellitus.

Other Endocrine Secretions

Besides the major endocrine glands already discussed, several other organs in the body possess varying degrees of endocrine function.

The **thymus gland**, located behind the manubrium of the sternum, is believed to secrete a hormone called thymosin, which helps the body's immune system to properly develop by influencing the maturation of certain white blood cells in the body, and their ability to produce antibodies for defense against infection. *(See Fig. 57)*

The **pineal** gland is a small structure located within the third ventricle of the brain. *(See Fig. 57)* Although its status as an endocrine gland is somewhat controversial, many scientists believe that it secretes hormones having effects on such things as ovarian function, adrenal cortex function, and normal brain physiology.

Even the kidneys and the heart put off hormones in the body. These organs produce hormones which have an effect on the important functions of blood pressure levels and red blood cell production.

THE NERVOUS SYSTEM
Chapter 13

Neurology

The word **neurology** is used in reference to the study of the nervous system. This system, or set of related organs, includes the brain, the spinal cord, and the cranial and spinal nerves.

The function of the nervous system as a whole is to provide a means by which all of the systems of the human body coordinate with one another. Messages are exchanged between the various body parts by way of the nervous system.

Neurons

The primary building block of the nervous system is the individual nerve cell. A single nerve cell is called a **neuron.** *(See Fig. 58)* A neuron is made of three distinct parts. Each neuron has a central section called the **cell body** and two or more filament-like extensions projecting from the cell body called **dendrites** and **axons.** The dendrites act as receiving units. They accept an electrical impulse generated from a nearby neuron. The impulse is passed through the cell body, and then on to the axon, which transmits the impulse on to the dendrite of another neuron. A small space is known to exist between the axon of one neuron and the dendrite of the next neuron. The small gap is called a **synapse.**

Nerves

Neurons are placed out end to end from one body part to another. The chain of neurons is surrounded by a non-nervous tissue called **neuroglia** (L. glia = glue). The combination of neurons and neuroglia creates a structure called a **nerve.**

Types of Nerves

There are many types of nerves in the human body. Those that consist of a single dendrite at one end of the nerve and a single axon at the other end are referred to as **bipolar neurons**. Nerves that have several dendrites at one end and a single axon on the other end are called **multipolar neurons**.

Nerves which transmit impulses from the brain or spinal cord to a body part causing the body part to function in some way are called **efferent** or **motor nerves**.

Nerves which relay messages from a body part back to the brain or spinal cord are called **afferent or sensory nerves**. These nerves detect pain, pressure, heat, texture, etc.

Subdivisions of the Nervous System

The whole nervous system of the human body is subdivided into two major portions. One portion is called the **central nervous system** and other is called the **peripheral nervous system**. The central nervous system consists of the brain and the spinal cord. These organs are both confined within the borders of the **dorsal cavity**. The peripheral nervous system is made up of the various cranial nerves emanating from the brain and the spinal nerves which extend from the spinal cord.

Parts of the Central Nervous System

The Brain

The scientific name for the brain is the **encephalon.** The outer surface of the encephalon appears to be wrinkled. *(See Fig. 59)* Actually the tissue consists of numerous elevations collectively called **gyri** and furrows called **sulci.** The brain tissue on the outside is sometimes referred to as **gray matter** and the tissue in the central portion is called **white matter**, due to their physical appearance to the eye. Gray matter is understood to be the location where intellectual activities occur. White matter is understood to be primarily involved in reflex and instinctual behavior activities.

Within the brain itself are four cavities called **ventricles.** They are identified as the right lateral, left lateral, third, and fourth ventricles. Each ventricle is lined with a group of specialized capillaries called the **choroid plexus.** The choroid plexus produces **cerebrospinal fluid**. This fluid, which is derived from the blood stream, is deposited into the **subarachnoid space** of the **meninges.** The meninges are membranes which cover the central nervous system and act as a cushion to protect the brain from mechanical trauma.

The **encephalon** is subdivided into four main sections. These four sections are the **cerebrum,** the **cerebellum,** the **brain stem**, and the **diencephalon.**

The Cerebrum

The largest of these sections is called the **cerebrum.** The cerebrum occupies almost all of the cranial cavity. *(See Fig. 59)* The cerebrum is divided into two equal portions called **hemispheres.** These hemispheres are created by a large longitudinal fissure which parallels the median plane of the body. The two hemispheres are held together near the floor of the cranial cavity by a structure called the **corpus callosum.** Each hemisphere of the cerebrum is further divided by a series of minor fissures creating four smaller structures called lobes. The lobes are labeled the **frontal, parietal, occipital**, and **temporal** lobes, due to their proximity to the various cranial bones by the same names.

The cerebrum is considered to be the center of the human intellect where processes like logic, reasoning and memory are ongoing.

The Cerebellum

The **cerebellum** is small portion of the encephalon which occupies the posterior and inferior portion of the cranial cavity. *(See Fig. 59)* The cerebellum is also divided into a right and left hemisphere but no further sub-divisions exist. The cerebellum is known to be the area of the brain which controls equilibrium and muscle coordination.

The Brain Stem

The **brain stem** is the most inferior portion of the encephalon. It lies inferior to the cerebrum and anterior to the cerebellum, and connects the other segments of the brain to the spinal cord. *(See Fig. 59)* The upper part of the brain stem is called the **mid-brain,** the middle segment the **pons varolii**, and the inferior segment the **medulla oblongata**. All three of these structures serve as important message relay centers between the brain and the spinal cord. Some important functions in the body controlled by the brain stem include respiration, heartbeat, and blood pressure levels.

The Diencephalon

The **diencephalon** is the final segment of the brain, consisting of two subdivisions called the **thalamus** and the **hypothalamus.** *(See Fig. 59)* The **thalamus** lies underneath the cerebrum, and is closely associated with the third ventricle of the brain, as each end of the thalamus is embedded in the lateral walls of the ventricle. The thalamus is believed to be important in relaying impulses from the sense organs of the body, including hearing, vision, taste, touch, and pain. The **hypothalamus,** which lies just below the thalamus and above the mid-brain, is a quite small but important section of the brain. It is closely associated with the pituitary gland, and has a controlling effect over the pituitary's release of its hormones. It also produces "anti-diuretic" hormone, which is stored by the posterior pituitary and released as needed into the bloodstream to help control the volume of water lost through the urinary system. The hypothalamus is also involved in regulating body temperature and is believed to affect some other activities, such as sleep cycles and appetite.

The Spinal Cord

The **spinal cord** is attached to the inferior end of the brain stem and is confined within the vertebral canal. The "solid" portion of the spinal cord extends from the foramen magnum of the occipital bone downward to about the second lumbar vertebra. From the second vertebra to the coccyx bone is a non-nervous tissue tip called the **filum terminal,** which is essentially an extension of the pia mater.

The external tissue of the spinal cord is composed of white matter like that occupying the interior of the encephalon. Inside of the spinal cord is an "H" shaped core of gray matter. It may be noted that the position of the gray and white matter in the brain and the spinal cord are the reverse of each other.

The entire central nervous system is surrounded by a set of protective membranes called the **meninges.** These membranes separate the encephalon from the cranial bones, and the spinal cord from the interior of the spinal canal.

The meninges are composed of three layers of tissue and a small space between two of the layers. The inner layer, closest to the brain, is called the **pia mater**. External to the pia mater is a small space called the subarachnoid space. This gap between layers is filled with cerebrospinal fluid. The second layer is called the arachnoid. The most external layer of the meninges is called the **dura mater**. This layer comes in contact with the bony inner surface of the cranium and spinal cord.

The Peripheral Nervous System

The Spinal Nerves

There are five groups of spinal nerves. Each group is called a plexus. The most superior group consists of eight pairs of spinal nerves called the cervical-brachial plexus. By themselves, nerves C-5 through T-1 are often called the brachial plexus, and serve to control the upper extremity.

There are twelve pairs of spinal nerves in the thoracic plexus which extend from the thoracic vertebrae. Five pairs of spinal nerves make up the lumbar plexus located between the vertebrae at the small of the back. Five more pairs make up the sacral plexus. One more pair makes up the so-called coccygeal plexus. There are a total of thirty-one pairs of spinal nerves in these five plexi. The nerves which extend from the lower end of the spinal cord do not leave the vertebrae immediately, but descend inferiorly through the vertebral canal like long strands of hair. This appearance is sometimes referred to as the **cauda equina** (horsetail) effect.

The Cranial Nerves

There are twelve pairs of cranial nerves which arise from the inferior surface of the encephalon and extend outward to various body tissues.

The cranial nerves are numbered #1 through #12 from front to back. The following table identifies each pair of nerves and their generally accepted area of responsibility.

TABLE N

Cranial Nerves and their Functions

CRANIAL NERVE	GENERAL FUNCTION
1. Olfactory nerve	Detection of odors
2. Optic nerve	Detection of light and color
3. Oculomotor nerve	Vertical and horizontal movement of the eyeball
4. Trochlear nerve	Diagonal movements of the eyeball
5. Trifacial nerve	Iris of the eye, maxillary and mandibular teeth gums, and lip
6. Abducent nerve	Lateral rectus muscle of the eyeball
7. Facial nerve	Skin of neck, scalp and external ear, taste buds and middle ear
8. Acoustic nerve	Detection of sound
9. Glossopharyngeal nerve	Muscles of the tongue
10. Vagus nerve	Sensory and motor nerve of the head, neck and torso
11. Accessory nerve	Muscles of the neck
12. Hypoglossal nerve	Muscles of the tongue

DEVELOPMENTAL ANATOMY
Chapter 14

The human body begins life as a single cell produced by the ovaries of the mother, and a single cell produced in the testes of the father. During the reproductive life of the woman, from puberty to menopause, except during pregnancy, her body releases an **ovum** (pl. **ova**) or **female gamete**, once a month. This ovum is commonly called an egg or female sex cell. This process is called **ovulation** and occurs about mid-way between a woman's menstrual periods. An **ovum**, or **oocyte**, is released approximately every 28 days. Since there is usually only one egg produced during ovulation, the two ovaries generally alternate in this function.

During **intercourse** the male deposits sperm in the woman's vagina. The sperm must then seek out the egg, if present. The egg must have begun its journey down the **fallopian** (or **uterine**) **tube** if it is going to unite with a sperm. When sperm encounter the egg, only one sperm is allowed to unite with the egg in a process called **fertilization.** Because of the short life span of an unfertilized egg, if fertilization is to occur it generally takes place in the fallopian tube, usually in the outer one-third of the tube.

Following fertilization many changes begin to occur to the egg. A fertilized egg is called a **zygote.** A zygote will undergo many cell divisions. As the cells divide they do so at a very rapid pace. So rapid are these divisions that they have not had time to grow and as such are smaller and smaller in size. The overall mass of cells remains about the size of the original egg. This mass of cells is now called a **morula.** The morula gets its name from its appearance, a mulberry-like mass of cells. As the cells continue to divide and grow they begin to migrate to the perimeter of the mass, and begin to resemble a hollow ball. The cavity within this "ball" is filled with fluid, and the mass is now called a **blastocyst** (or **blastula**). At one end of the blastocyst an area of cells becomes thicker. This is the area that will become the placenta and will give rise to the **embryonic mass.**

The **placenta** is that structure that serves as the connecting link to the mother's body. It is like a plug into the mother's endometrium which allows for the passing of nutrients and wastes between baby and mother. Within the placenta, the mother's blood and the baby's blood come into close contact but do not mix. The blastocyst will eventually attach itself to the **endometrium,** or the inner lining of the uterus. This process is called **implantation,** and it occurs about ten days to two weeks following fertilization. It has taken the egg this long to make the journey from the ovary, through the fallopian tube, and into the uterus.

Following implantation many changes continue to occur. The embryonic mass begins to sprout and, from this area, the embryo begins to form. Its layers are referred to as **embryonic** (or **primary**) **germ layers**. The outer layer is called the **ectoderm,** the middle layer is called **mesoderm,** and the innermost layer is the **endoderm.** Each of these layers gives rise to different body structures. The embryo continues to develop, progressively taking on the appearance of a minia-ture human being. Head, arms, and legs are all beginning to take shape after only four weeks, but the embryo's size is only about one-fourth of an inch long.

TABLE
Primary Germ Layers and Their Results

Ectoderm	Mesoderm	Endoderm
Nerve tissue of the brain, spinal chord, and nerves	Connective tissue of bone, cartilage, blood cells, and lymph	Epithelium of the alimentary canal and respiratory system (except as noted), urinary bladder and urethra
Epidermis and its appendages	Muscle tissue	
Epithelial linings of mouth, nose, and anal canal	Epithelium of the vessels kidneys, ureters, and body cavities	

At about the beginning of the third **lunar month** (a lunar month is 28 days), the baby is no longer referred to as an embryo, but is now called a **fetus.** The fetus continues to grow very rapidly at a rate of about two inches in length each month until birth. At birth the baby will be approximately twenty inches long.

Remember that during the period of **gestation** (development inside the moth-er's body) the fetus is dependent on its mother for all nourishment, including its breathing. The mother's blood will pass oxygen as well as nutrients across the placenta. Because of this, several things are different during fetal circulation.

Fetal Circulation

During the fetal period, the baby does not breathe or eat on its own, but does so only through the placenta connected to mother's body. Because of this, and the fact that many of the structures in the fetus's body are not fully developed, nature has incorporated some variations in the circulatory system.

During fetal circulation the **umbilical vein** serves to carry oxygen and nutri-ents from the placenta to the baby. After passing through the umbilicus into the baby's body, the umbilical vein gives off a branch called the **ductus venosus**. The ductus venosus acts as a shortcut to bypass the liver, allowing some of the blood to go directly into the **inferior vena cava**. When the umbilical cord is tied, this vessel has no useful function, so it atrophies and becomes known as the **ligamentum venosum** in an adult. After giving off the ductus venosus as a branch, the umbilical vein continues until it empties into the portal vein, allowing blood to pass through the baby's liver. As with the ductus venosus, when the umbilical cord is tied, the portion of the umbilical vein which remains inside the baby's body has no function, so it too atrophies and becomes known as the **ligamentum teres** of the liver.

In the fetal heart there is an opening in the atrial septum called the **foramen ovale.** This shortcut allows about one-third of the blood entering the right atrium to pass directly into the left atrium, bypassing the pulmonary system. Remember, this blood has already received its oxygen in the placenta, and does not need to go to the lungs for oxygenation. The opening closes shortly after birth, and all that remains is a small depression referred to as the **fossa ovalis.** Blood, which entered the right atrium, but did not pass through the foramen ovale, enters the right ventricle and is pumped out into the pulmonary artery. However, as this blood does not need to go to the lungs for oxygen, most of it is diverted out of the pulmonary artery by another shortcut called the **ductus arteriosus.** The ductus arteriosus empties blood directly into the aortic arch. It also closes down after birth, atrophies, and becomes known as the **ligamentum arteriosum.**

In order to receive more oxygen and nutrients, the fetal blood must again leave the baby's body and return to the placenta. This is accomplished by the two fetal umbilical arteries, which branch off from the child's internal iliac arteries. These two vessels exit through the umbilical area and wrap around the outside of the umbilical vein as they head toward the placenta. As with the umbilical vein, these arteries serve no purpose after the umbilical cord has been cut, and will atrophy to become known as the **lateral umbilical ligaments** in an adult.

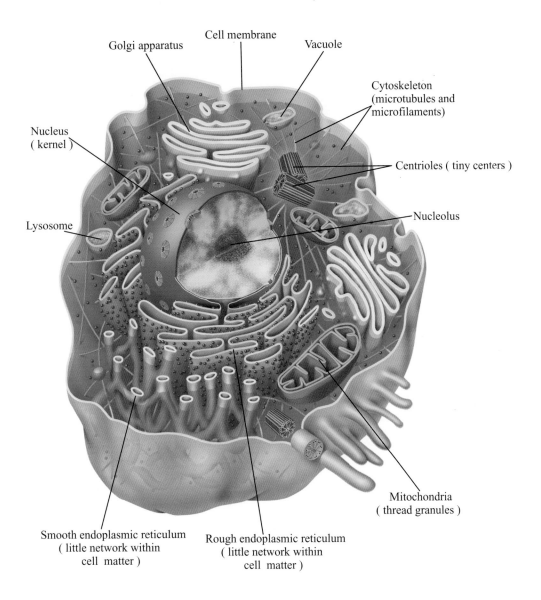

Golgi apparatus

Cell membrane

Vacuole

Cytoskeleton
(microtubules and
microfilaments)

Nucleus
(kernel)

Centrioles (tiny centers)

Lysosome

Nucleolus

Mitochondria
(thread granules)

Smooth endoplasmic reticulum
(little network within
cell matter)

Rough endoplasmic reticulum
(little network within
cell matter)

Figure 1 – The Cell

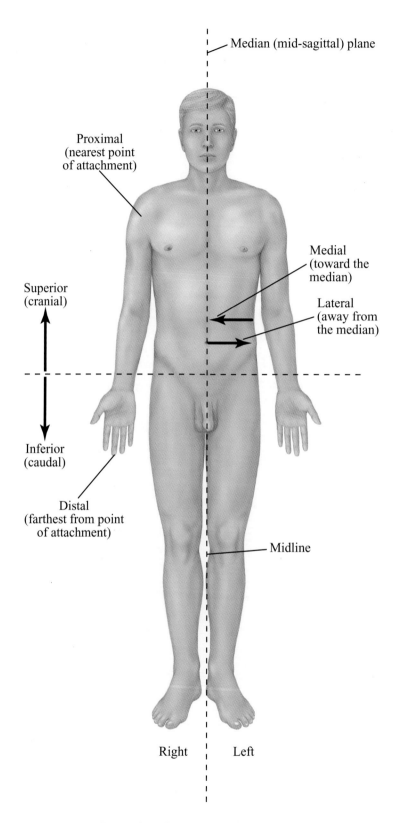

Median (mid-sagittal) plane

Proximal
(nearest point
of attachment)

Medial
(toward the
median)

Lateral
(away from
the median)

Superior
(cranial)

Inferior
(caudal)

Distal
(farthest from point
of attachment)

Midline

Right　Left

Figure 2 – The Anatomical Position

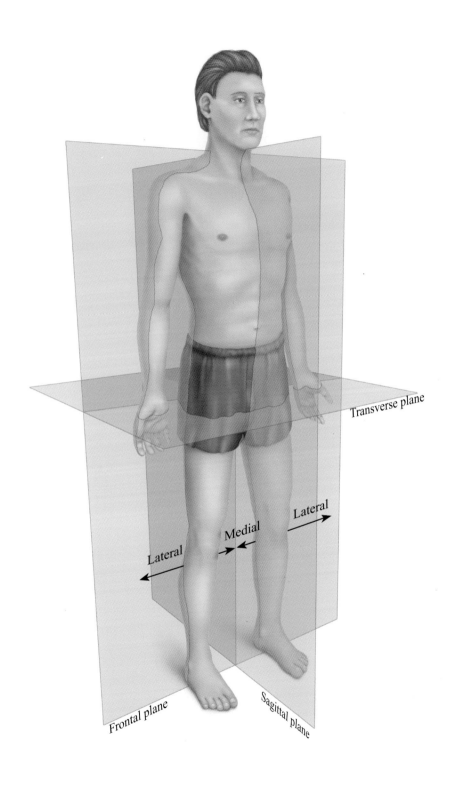

Figure 3 – Body Planes

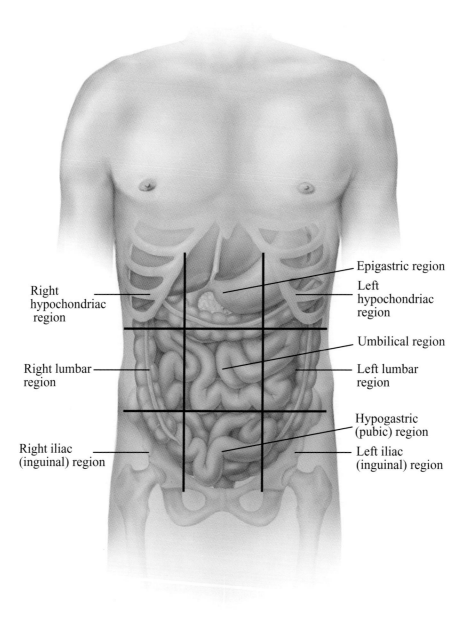

Right
hypochondriac
region

Right lumbar
region

Right iliac
(inguinal) region

Epigastric region

Left
hypochondriac
region

Umbilical region

Left lumbar
region

Hypogastric
(pubic) region

Left iliac
(inguinal) region

Figure 4 – Abdominal Regions

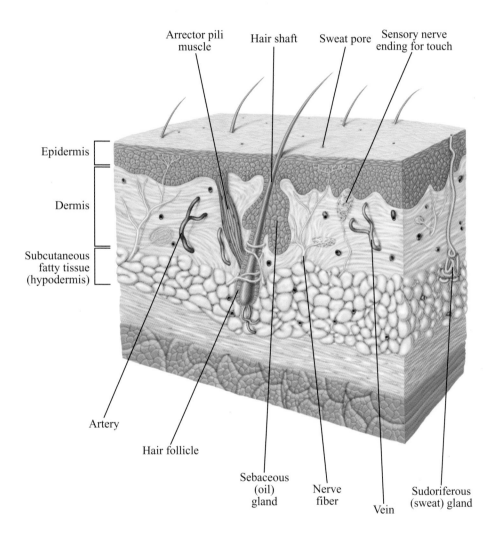

Arrector pili
muscle

Hair shaft

Sweat pore

Sensory nerve
ending for touch

Epidermis

Dermis

Subcutaneous
fatty tissue
(hypodermis)

Artery

Hair follicle

Sebaceous
(oil)
gland

Nerve
fiber

Vein

Sudoriferous
(sweat) gland

Figure 5 – The Skin

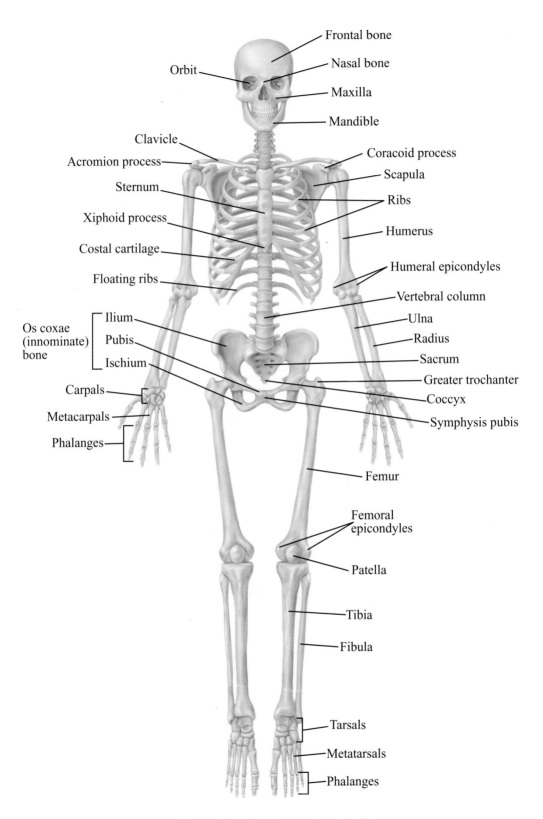

Frontal bone

Nasal bone

Maxilla

Mandible

Orbit

Clavicle

Acromion process

Coracoid process

Scapula

Sternum

Ribs

Xiphoid process

Humerus

Costal cartilage

Floating ribs

Humeral epicondyles

Vertebral column

Os coxae
(innominate)
bone

Ilium

Pubis

Ischium

Ulna

Radius

Sacrum

Greater trochanter

Coccyx

Carpals

Metacarpals

Phalanges

Symphysis pubis

Femur

Femoral
epicondyles

Patella

Tibia

Fibula

Tarsals

Metatarsals

Phalanges

Figure 6 – The Skeleton –Anterior View

110

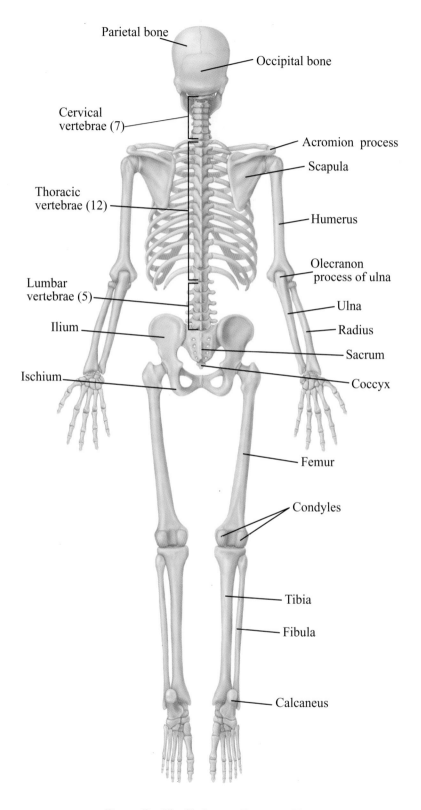

Parietal bone

Occipital bone

Cervical
vertebrae (7)

Acromion process

Scapula

Thoracic
vertebrae (12)

Humerus

Olecranon
process of ulna

Lumbar
vertebrae (5)

Ulna

Ilium

Radius

Sacrum

Ischium

Coccyx

Femur

Condyles

Tibia

Fibula

Calcaneus

Figure 7 – The Skeleton – Posterior View

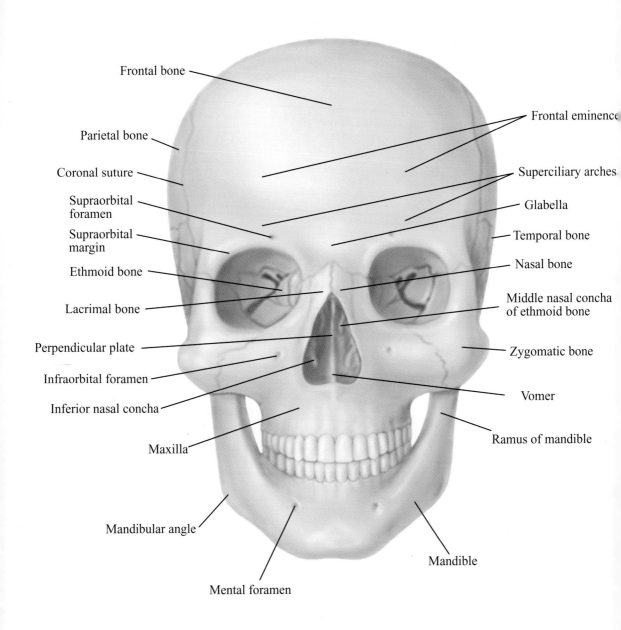

Frontal bone

Parietal bone

Coronal suture

Supraorbital
foramen

Supraorbital
margin

Ethmoid bone

Lacrimal bone

Perpendicular plate

Infraorbital foramen

Inferior nasal concha

Maxilla

Mandibular angle

Mental foramen

Frontal eminence

Superciliary arches

Glabella

Temporal bone

Nasal bone

Middle nasal concha
of ethmoid bone

Zygomatic bone

Vomer

Ramus of mandible

Mandible

Figure 8 – The Skull – Anterior View

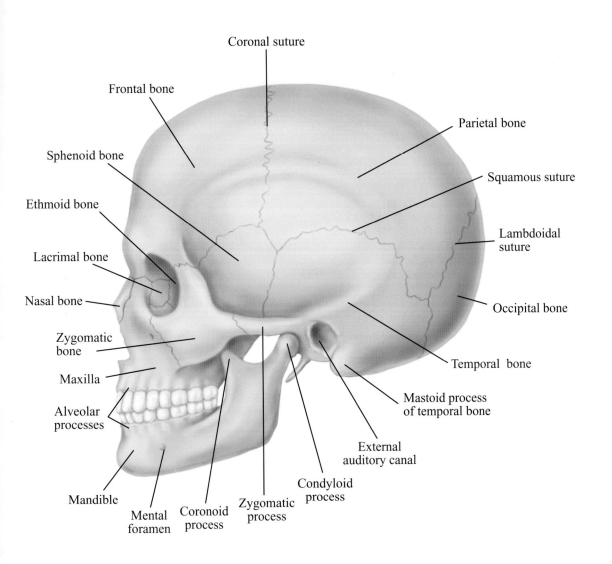

Coronal suture

Frontal bone

Sphenoid bone

Ethmoid bone

Lacrimal bone

Nasal bone

Zygomatic
bone

Maxilla

Alveolar
processes

Mandible

Mental
foramen

Coronoid
process

Zygomatic
process

Condyloid
process

External
auditory canal

Mastoid process
of temporal bone

Temporal bone

Occipital bone

Lambdoidal
suture

Squamous suture

Parietal bone

Figure 9 – The Skull – Lateral View

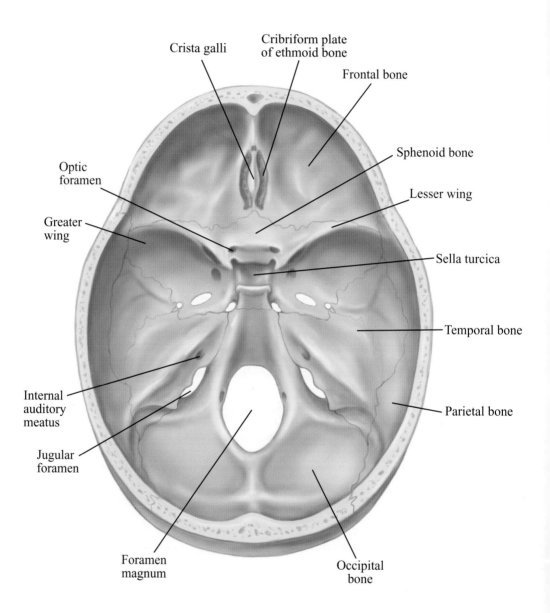

Crista galli

Cribriform plate
of ethmoid bone

Frontal bone

Sphenoid bone

Optic
foramen

Lesser wing

Greater
wing

Sella turcica

Temporal bone

Internal
auditory
meatus

Parietal bone

Jugular
foramen

Foramen
magnum

Occipital
bone

Figure 10 – The Skull – Interior View

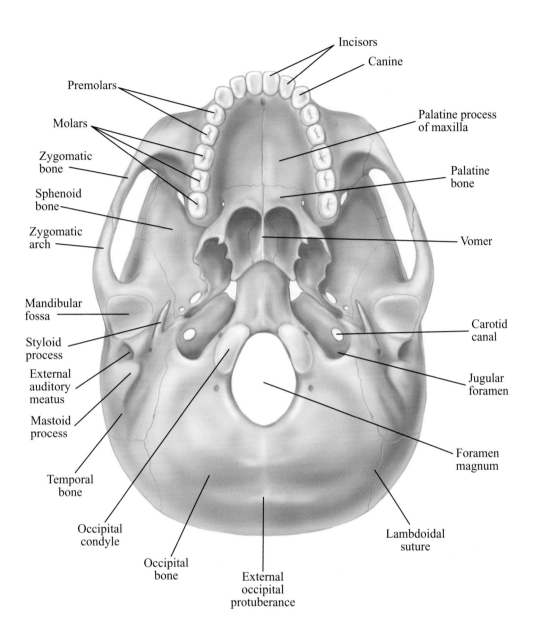

Incisors

Canine

Premolars

Palatine process
of maxilla

Molars

Zygomatic
bone

Palatine
bone

Sphenoid
bone

Zygomatic
arch

Vomer

Mandibular
fossa

Carotid
canal

Styloid
process

Jugular
foramen

External
auditory
meatus

Mastoid
process

Temporal
bone

Foramen
magnum

Occipital
condyle

Lambdoidal
suture

Occipital
bone

External
occipital
protuberance

Figure 11 – The Skull – Inferior View

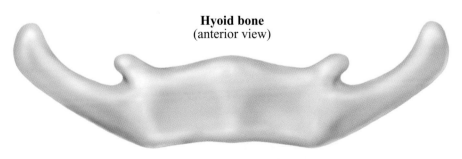

Hyoid bone
(anterior view)

Figure 12 – The Hyoid Bone

115

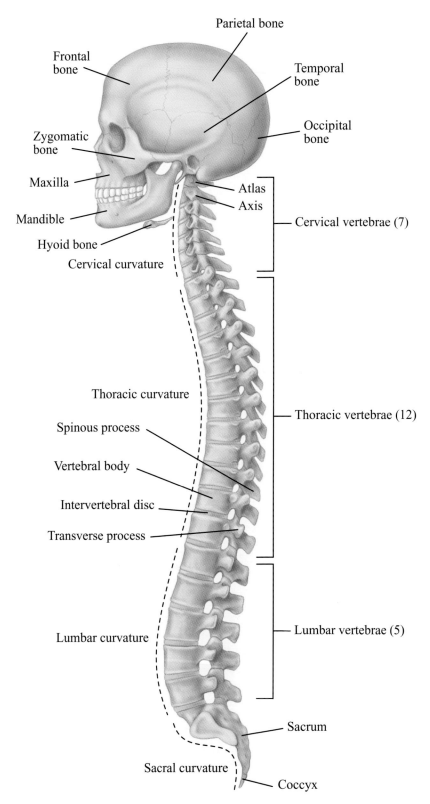

Parietal bone

Frontal bone

Temporal bone

Zygomatic bone

Occipital bone

Maxilla

Atlas

Mandible

Axis

Hyoid bone

Cervical vertebrae (7)

Cervical curvature

Thoracic curvature

Spinous process

Thoracic vertebrae (12)

Vertebral body

Intervertebral disc

Transverse process

Lumbar vertebrae (5)

Lumbar curvature

Sacrum

Sacral curvature

Coccyx

Figure 13 – The Vertebral Column

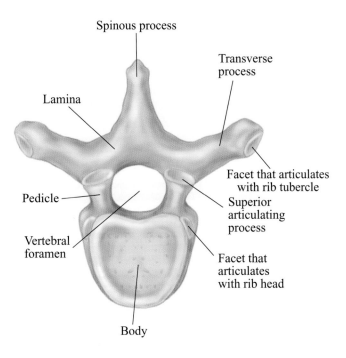

Spinous process

Transverse process

Lamina

Facet that articulates with rib tubercle

Pedicle

Superior articulating process

Vertebral foramen

Facet that articulates with rib head

Body

Figure 14 – Thoracie Vertebra

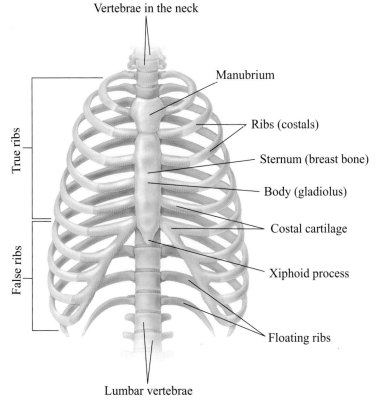

Vertebrae in the neck

Manubrium

True ribs

Ribs (costals)

Sternum (breast bone)

Body (gladiolus)

Costal cartilage

False ribs

Xiphoid process

Floating ribs

Lumbar vertebrae

Figure 15 – The Ribs and Sternum

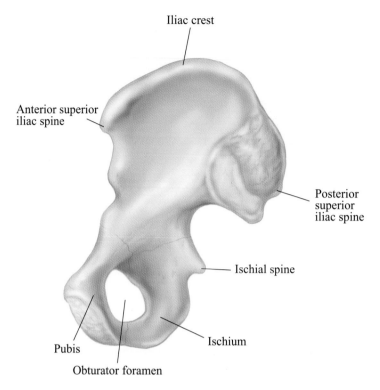

Iliac crest

Anterior superior
iliac spine

Posterior
superior
iliac spine

Ischial spine

Ischium

Pubis

Obturator foramen

Figure 16 – The Os Coxa - Medial View

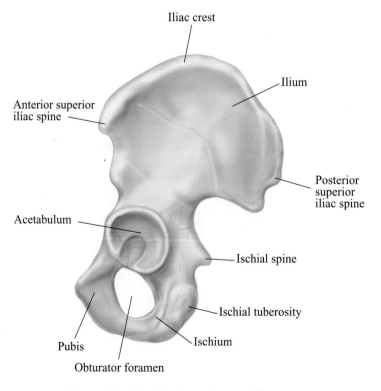

Iliac crest

Ilium

Anterior superior
iliac spine

Posterior
superior
iliac spine

Acetabulum

Ischial spine

Ischial tuberosity

Ischium

Pubis

Obturator foramen

Figure 17 – The Os Coxa - Lateral View

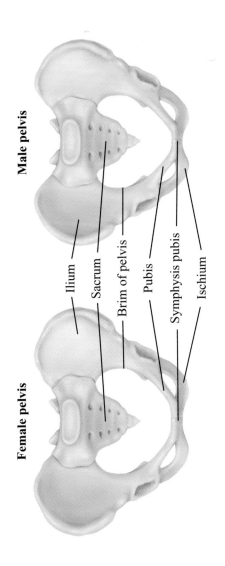

Figure 18 – Female vs. Male Pelvis

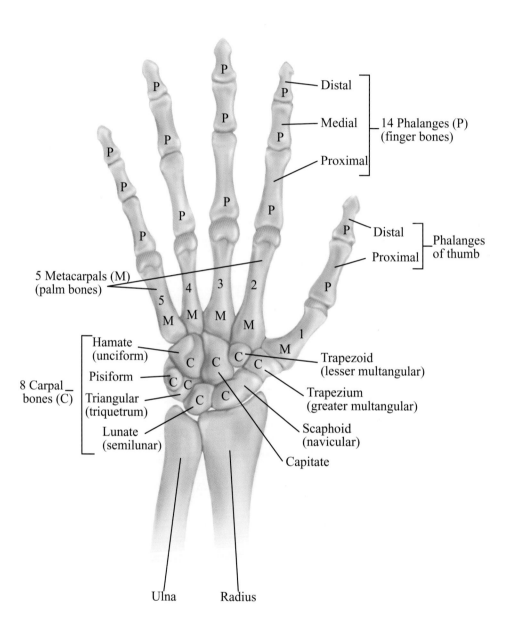

Distal

Medial

Proximal

14 Phalanges (P)
(finger bones)

Distal

Proximal

Phalanges
of thumb

5 Metacarpals (M)
(palm bones)

5
4
3
2
M M M M

1
M

Hamate
(unciform)

Pisiform

Triangular
(triquetrum)

Lunate
(semilunar)

8 Carpal
bones (C)

C C C
C C
C C

Trapezoid
(lesser multangular)

Trapezium
(greater multangular)

Scaphoid
(navicular)

Capitate

Ulna   Radius

Figure 19 – Bones of the Hand and Wrist

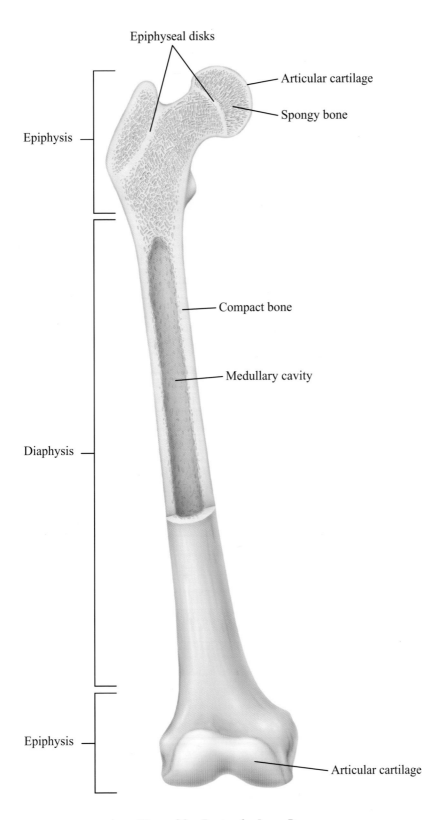

Figure 20 – Parts of a Long Bone

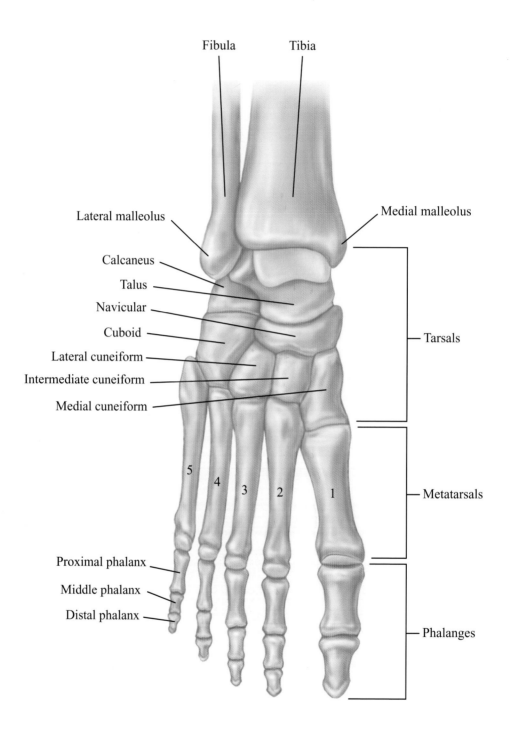

Fibula   Tibia

Lateral malleolus   Medial malleolus

Calcaneus

Talus

Navicular

Cuboid

Lateral cuneiform

Intermediate cuneiform

Medial cuneiform

Tarsals

5   4   3   2   1

Metatarsals

Proximal phalanx

Middle phalanx

Distal phalanx

Phalanges

Figure 21 – Bones of the Foot and Ankle

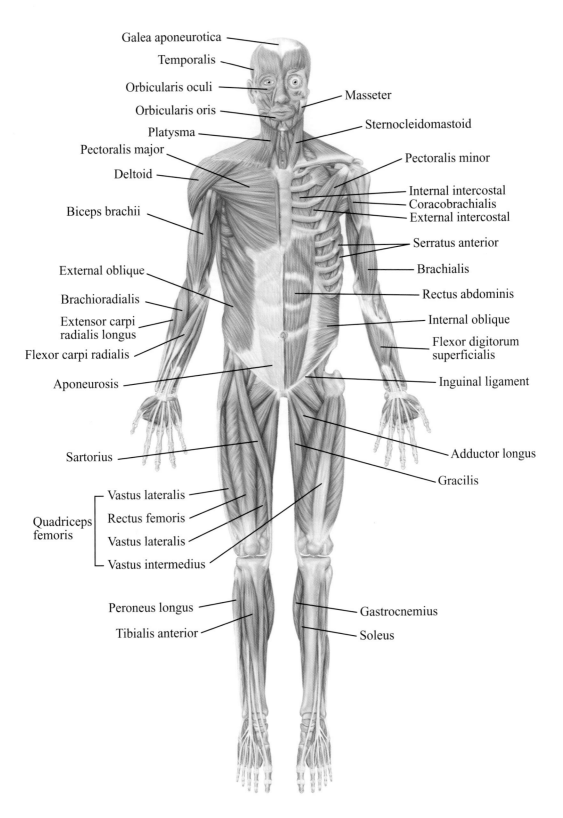

Galea aponeurotica
Temporalis
Orbicularis oculi
Orbicularis oris
Platysma
Pectoralis major
Deltoid
Biceps brachii
External oblique
Brachioradialis
Extensor carpi
radialis longus
Flexor carpi radialis
Aponeurosis
Sartorius
Quadriceps
femoris
Vastus lateralis
Rectus femoris
Vastus lateralis
Vastus intermedius
Peroneus longus
Tibialis anterior

Masseter
Sternocleidomastoid
Pectoralis minor
Internal intercostal
Coracobrachialis
External intercostal
Serratus anterior
Brachialis
Rectus abdominis
Internal oblique
Flexor digitorum
superficialis
Inguinal ligament
Adductor longus
Gracilis
Gastrocnemius
Soleus

Figure 22 – Muscles of the Body – Anterior View

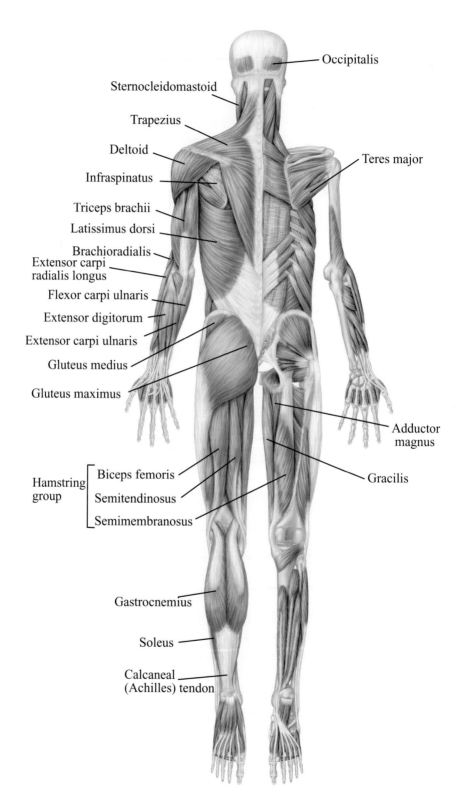

Occipitalis

Sternocleidomastoid

Trapezius

Deltoid

Infraspinatus

Triceps brachii

Latissimus dorsi

Brachioradialis

Extensor carpi
radialis longus

Flexor carpi ulnaris

Extensor digitorum

Extensor carpi ulnaris

Gluteus medius

Gluteus maximus

Teres major

Adductor
magnus

Gracilis

Hamstring
group

Biceps femoris

Semitendinosus

Semimembranosus

Gastrocnemius

Soleus

Calcaneal
(Achilles) tendon

Figure 23 – Muscles of the Body – Posterior View

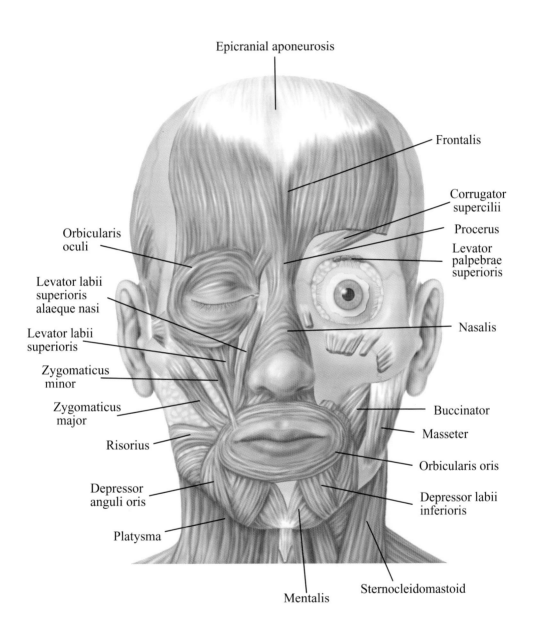

Epicranial aponeurosis

Frontalis

Corrugator
supercilii

Procerus

Levator
palpebrae
superioris

Orbicularis
oculi

Levator labii
superioris
alaeque nasi

Nasalis

Levator labii
superioris

Zygomaticus
minor

Zygomaticus
major

Buccinator

Risorius

Masseter

Orbicularis oris

Depressor
anguli oris

Depressor labii
inferioris

Platysma

Sternocleidomastoid

Mentalis

Figure 24 – Muscles of the Face

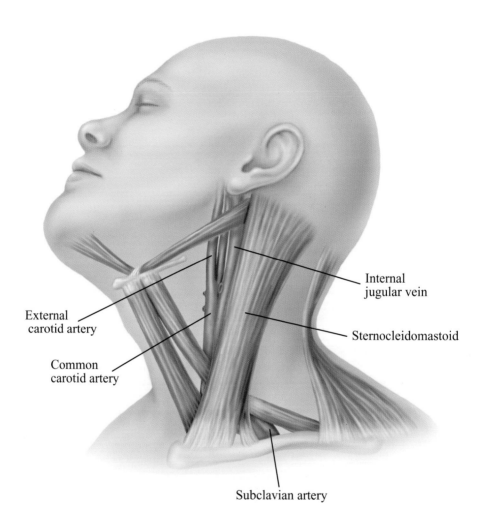

Internal
jugular vein

External
carotid artery

Common
carotid artery

Sternocleidomastoid

Subclavian artery

Figure 25 – Muscles of the Neck

126

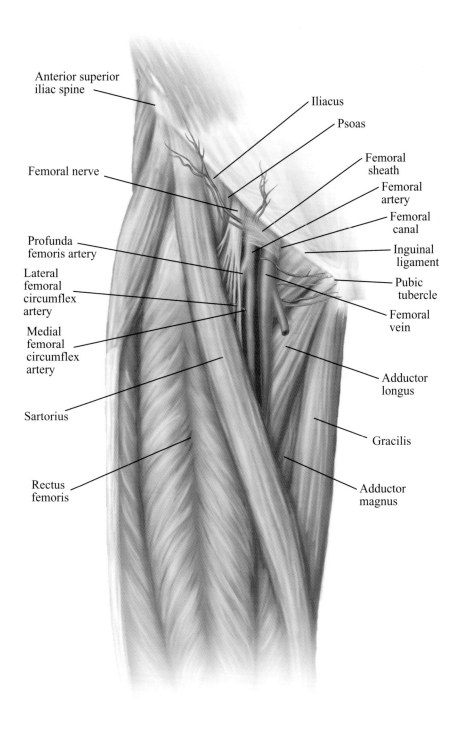

Anterior superior
iliac spine

Femoral nerve

Profunda
femoris artery

Lateral
femoral
circumflex
artery

Medial
femoral
circumflex
artery

Sartorius

Rectus
femoris

Iliacus

Psoas

Femoral
sheath

Femoral
artery

Femoral
canal

Inguinal
ligament

Pubic
tubercle

Femoral
vein

Adductor
longus

Gracilis

Adductor
magnus

Figure 26 – Femoral Triangle – Right Lower Extremity

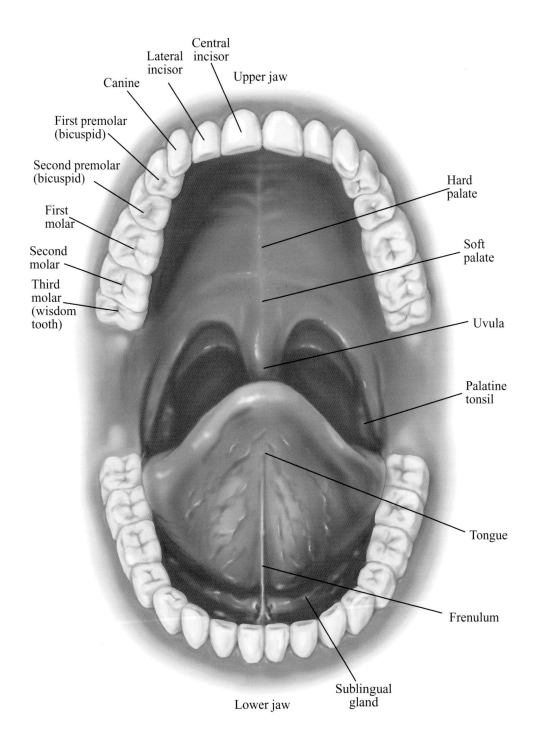

Canine

Lateral
incisor

Central
incisor

Upper jaw

First premolar
(bicuspid)

Second premolar
(bicuspid)

First
molar

Second
molar

Third
molar
(wisdom
tooth)

Hard
palate

Soft
palate

Uvula

Palatine
tonsil

Tongue

Frenulum

Sublingual
gland

Lower jaw

Figure 27 – The Mouth

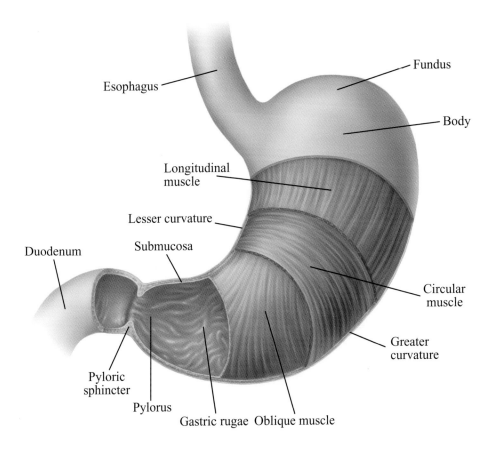

Esophagus

Fundus

Body

Longitudinal
muscle

Lesser curvature

Duodenum

Submucosa

Circular
muscle

Greater
curvature

Pyloric
sphincter

Pylorus

Gastric rugae Oblique muscle

Figure 28 – The Stomach

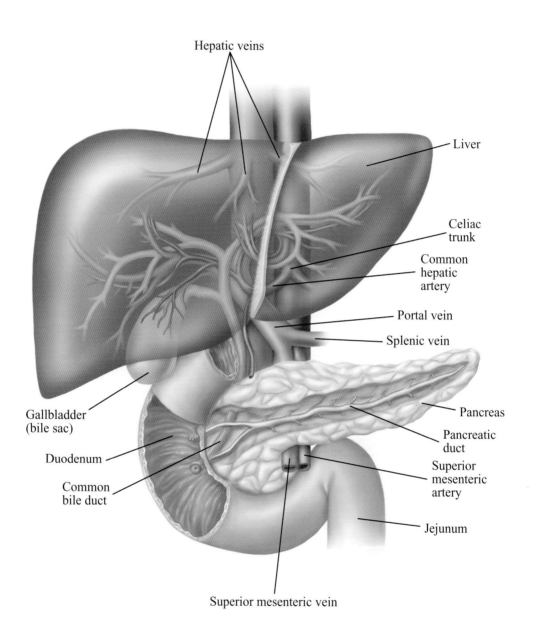

Hepatic veins

Liver

Celiac trunk

Common hepatic artery

Portal vein

Splenic vein

Gallbladder (bile sac)

Pancreas

Pancreatic duct

Duodenum

Superior mesenteric artery

Common bile duct

Jejunum

Superior mesenteric vein

Figure 29 – The Liver, Gall Bladder and Pancreas

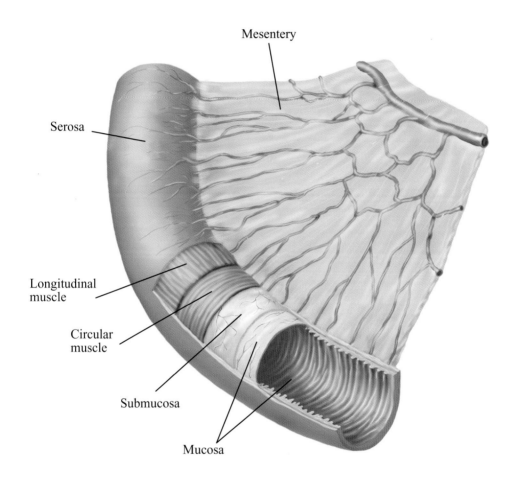

Mesentery

Serosa

Longitudinal
muscle

Circular
muscle

Submucosa

Mucosa

Figure 30 – The Small Intestine

131

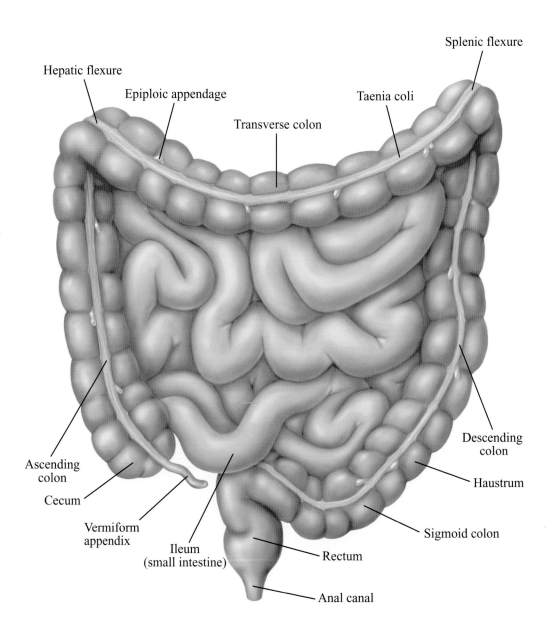

Hepatic flexure

Epiploic appendage

Transverse colon

Taenia coli

Splenic flexure

Ascending colon

Cecum

Vermiform appendix

Ileum (small intestine)

Rectum

Descending colon

Haustrum

Sigmoid colon

Anal canal

Figure 31 – The Large Intestine

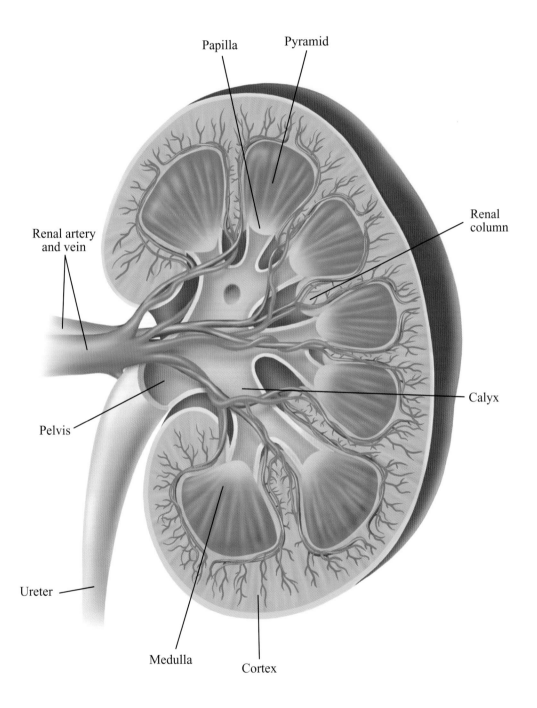

Papilla

Pyramid

Renal
column

Renal artery
and vein

Calyx

Pelvis

Ureter

Medulla

Cortex

Figure 32– The Kidney

133

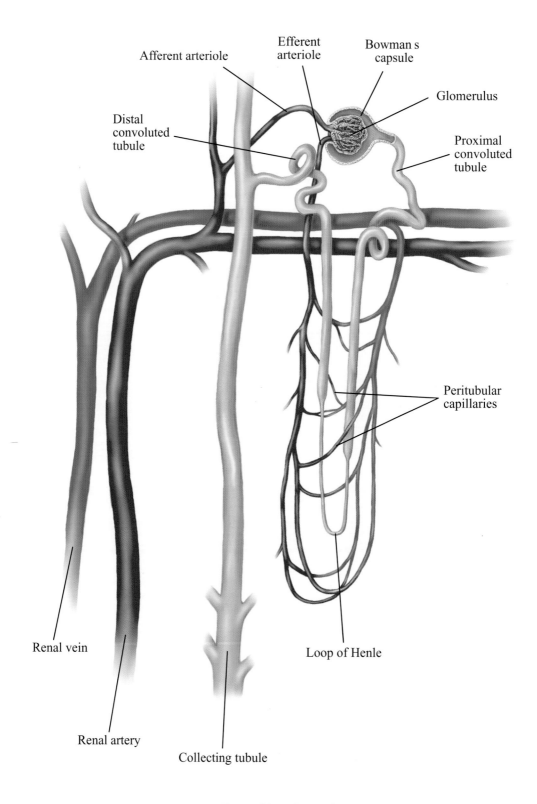

Afferent arteriole

Efferent arteriole

Bowman s capsule

Glomerulus

Distal convoluted tubule

Proximal convoluted tubule

Peritubular capillaries

Renal vein

Loop of Henle

Renal artery

Collecting tubule

Figure 33 – The Nephron

134

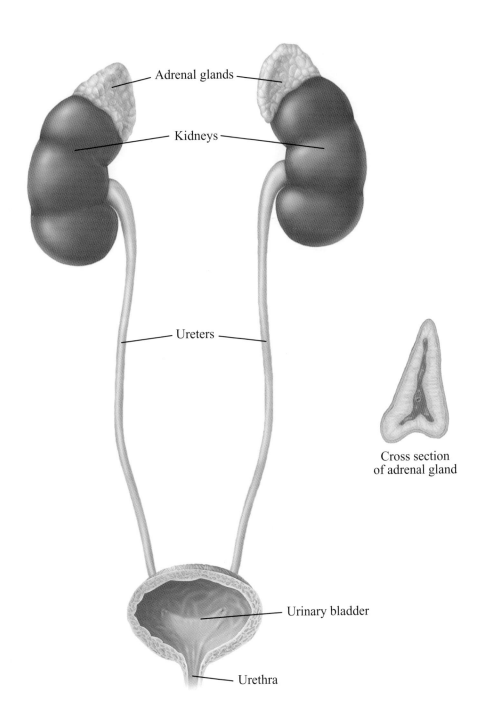

Adrenal glands

Kidneys

Ureters

Cross section
of adrenal gland

Urinary bladder

Urethra

Figure 34 – The Urinary System

135

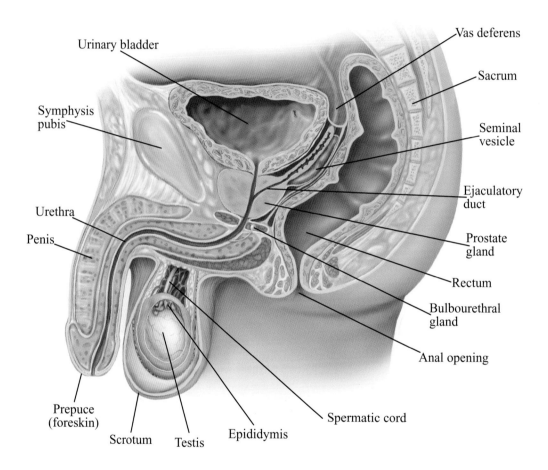

Urinary bladder

Symphysis
pubis

Urethra

Penis

Prepuce
(foreskin)

Scrotum

Testis

Epididymis

Spermatic cord

Vas deferens

Sacrum

Seminal
vesicle

Ejaculatory
duct

Prostate
gland

Rectum

Bulbourethral
gland

Anal opening

Figure 35 – Male Pelvic Region

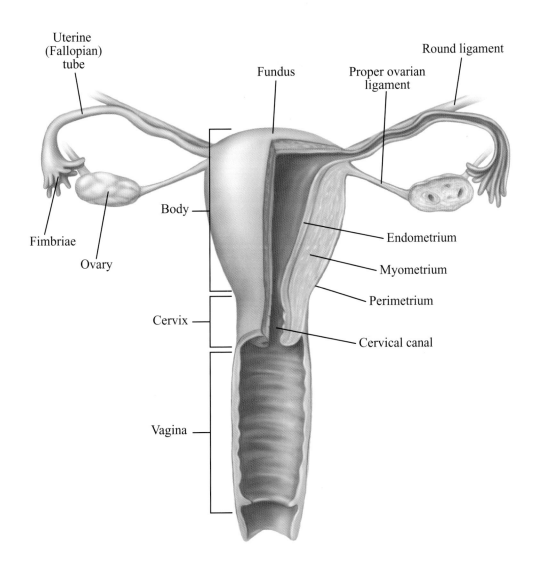

Uterine
(Fallopian)
tube

Fundus

Proper ovarian
ligament

Round ligament

Fimbriae

Ovary

Body

Endometrium

Myometrium

Perimetrium

Cervix

Cervical canal

Vagina

Figure 36 – Female Reproductive Tract

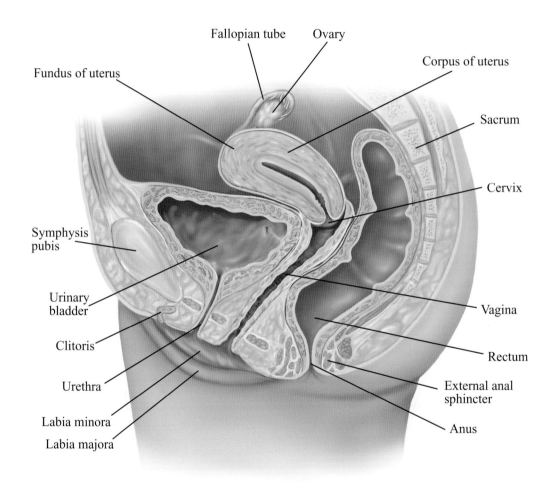

Fallopian tube   Ovary

Fundus of uterus

Corpus of uterus

Sacrum

Symphysis pubis

Cervix

Urinary bladder

Clitoris

Urethra

Labia minora

Labia majora

Vagina

Rectum

External anal sphincter

Anus

Figure 37 – Female Relvic Region

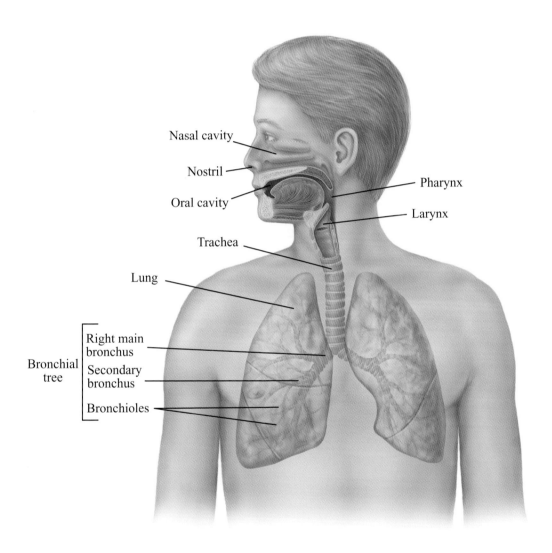

Nasal cavity

Nostril

Oral cavity

Pharynx

Larynx

Trachea

Lung

Bronchial
tree

Right main
bronchus

Secondary
bronchus

Bronchioles

Figure 38 – Respiratory System

139

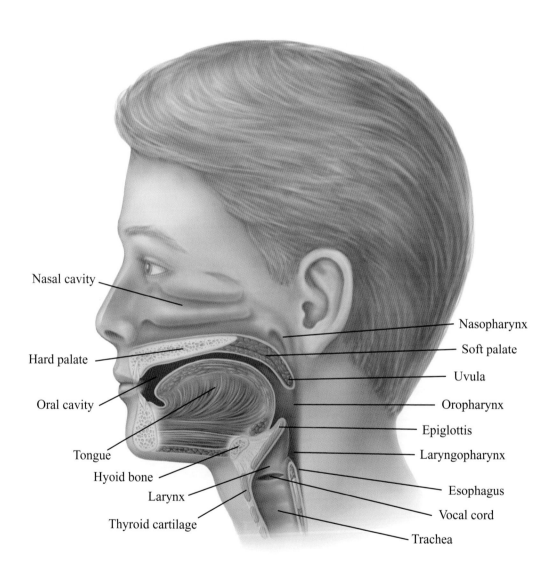

Nasal cavity

Hard palate

Oral cavity

Tongue

Hyoid bone

Larynx

Thyroid cartilage

Nasopharynx

Soft palate

Uvula

Oropharynx

Epiglottis

Laryngopharynx

Esophagus

Vocal cord

Trachea

Figure 39– The Pharynx and the Larynx

Red blood cells (erythrocytes)

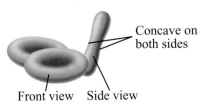

Concave on both sides

Front view   Side view

White blood cells (leukocytes)

Granulocytes

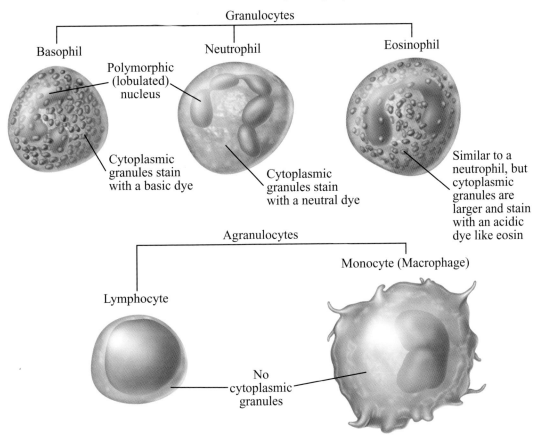

Basophil

Neutrophil

Eosinophil

Polymorphic (lobulated) nucleus

Cytoplasmic granules stain with a basic dye

Cytoplasmic granules stain with a neutral dye

Similar to a neutrophil, but cytoplasmic granules are larger and stain with an acidic dye like eosin

Agranulocytes

Monocyte (Macrophage)

Lymphocyte

No cytoplasmic granules

Platelets

Figure 40 – The Blood Cells

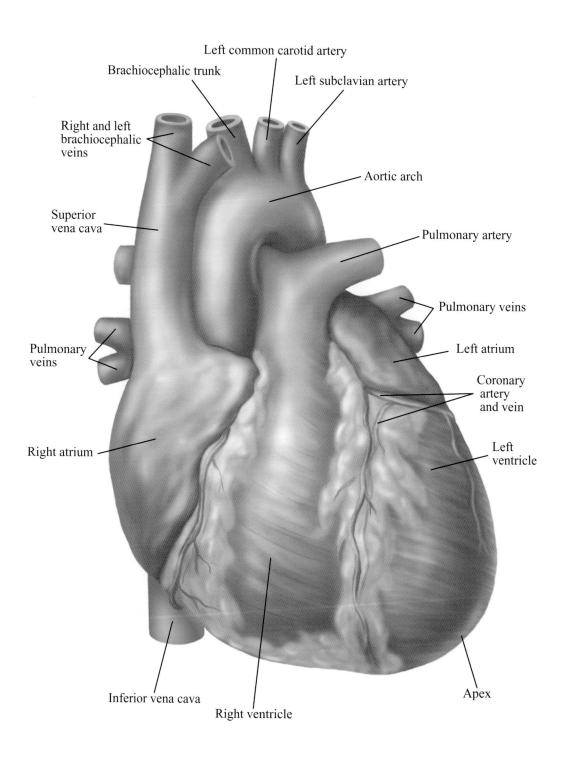

Left common carotid artery

Brachiocephalic trunk

Left subclavian artery

Right and left
brachiocephalic
veins

Aortic arch

Superior
vena cava

Pulmonary artery

Pulmonary veins

Pulmonary
veins

Left atrium

Coronary
artery
and vein

Right atrium

Left
ventricle

Inferior vena cava

Apex

Right ventricle

Figure 41– The Heart – Exterior View

142

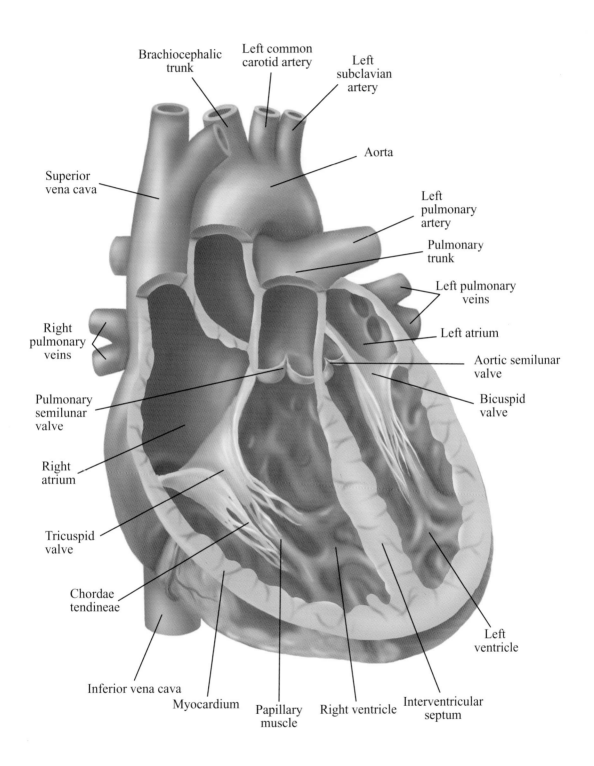

Brachiocephalic trunk

Left common carotid artery

Left subclavian artery

Superior vena cava

Aorta

Left pulmonary artery

Pulmonary trunk

Left pulmonary veins

Right pulmonary veins

Left atrium

Aortic semilunar valve

Pulmonary semilunar valve

Bicuspid valve

Right atrium

Tricuspid valve

Chordae tendineae

Left ventricle

Inferior vena cava

Myocardium

Papillary muscle

Right ventricle

Interventricular septum

Figure 42– The Heart – Interior View

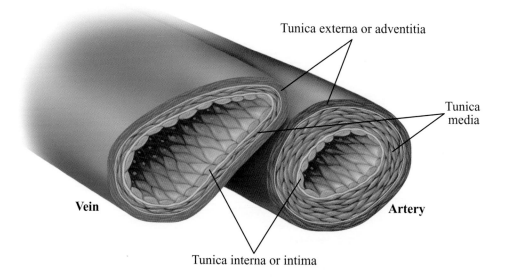

Tunica externa or adventitia

Tunica media

Tunica interna or intima

Vein

Artery

Figure 43– Vessel Layers

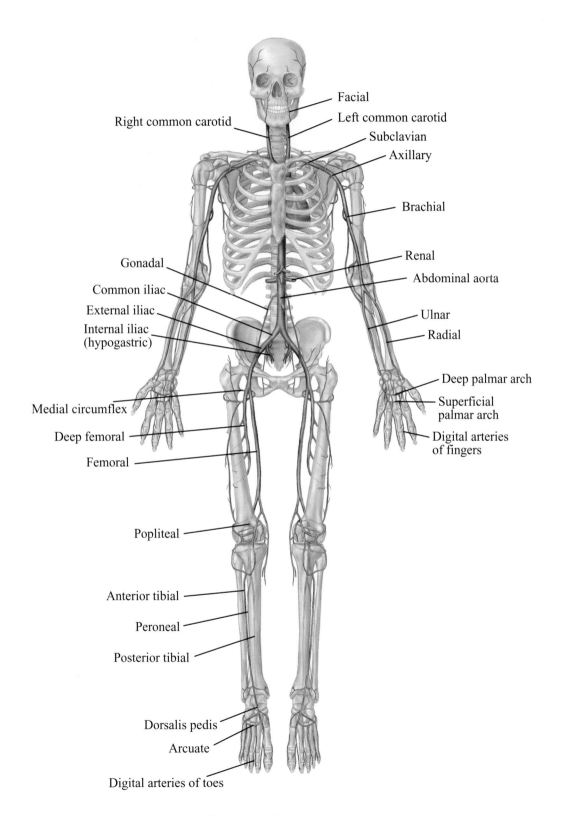

Right common carotid

Facial

Left common carotid

Subclavian

Axillary

Brachial

Gonadal

Common iliac

External iliac

Internal iliac
(hypogastric)

Renal

Abdominal aorta

Ulnar

Radial

Deep palmar arch

Superficial
palmar arch

Digital arteries
of fingers

Medial circumflex

Deep femoral

Femoral

Popliteal

Anterior tibial

Peroneal

Posterior tibial

Dorsalis pedis

Arcuate

Digital arteries of toes

Figure 44– The Arteries

145

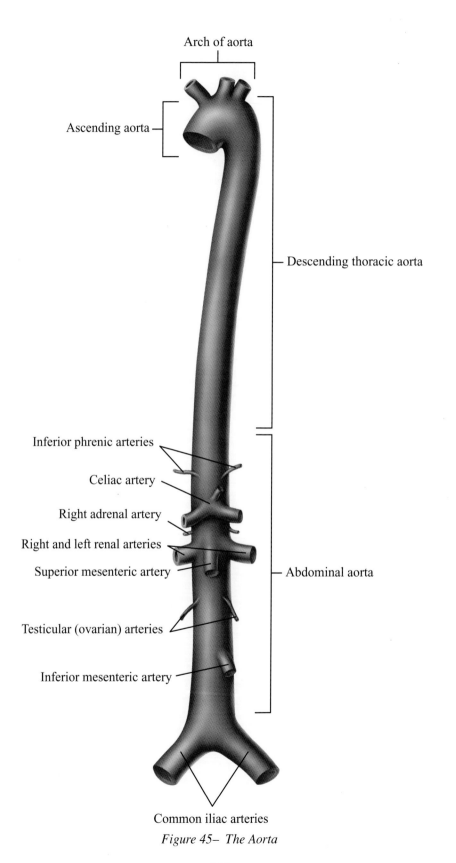

Arch of aorta

Ascending aorta

Descending thoracic aorta

Inferior phrenic arteries

Celiac artery

Right adrenal artery

Right and left renal arteries

Superior mesenteric artery

Abdominal aorta

Testicular (ovarian) arteries

Inferior mesenteric artery

Common iliac arteries

Figure 45– The Aorta

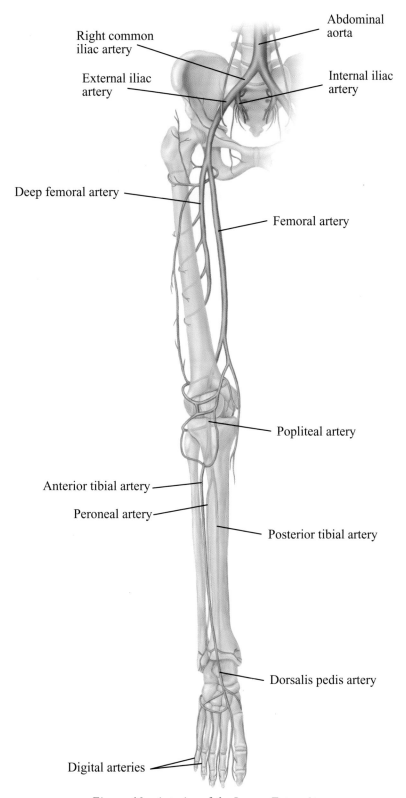

Right common
iliac artery

Abdominal
aorta

External iliac
artery

Internal iliac
artery

Deep femoral artery

Femoral artery

Popliteal artery

Anterior tibial artery

Peroneal artery

Posterior tibial artery

Dorsalis pedis artery

Digital arteries

Figure 46– Arteries of the Lower Extremity

147

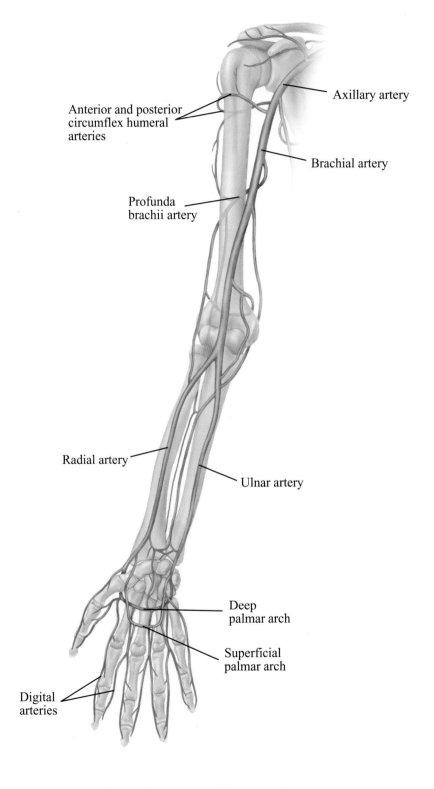

Anterior and posterior circumflex humeral arteries

Axillary artery

Brachial artery

Profunda brachii artery

Radial artery

Ulnar artery

Deep palmar arch

Superficial palmar arch

Digital arteries

Figure 47– Arteries of the Upper Extremity

148

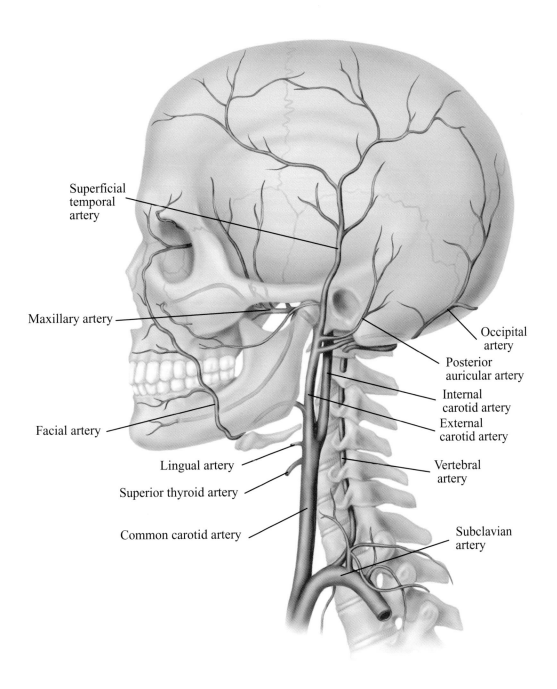

Superficial
temporal
artery

Maxillary artery

Facial artery

Lingual artery

Superior thyroid artery

Common carotid artery

Occipital
artery

Posterior
auricular artery

Internal
carotid artery

External
carotid artery

Vertebral
artery

Subclavian
artery

Figure 48– Arteries of the Head and Neck

149

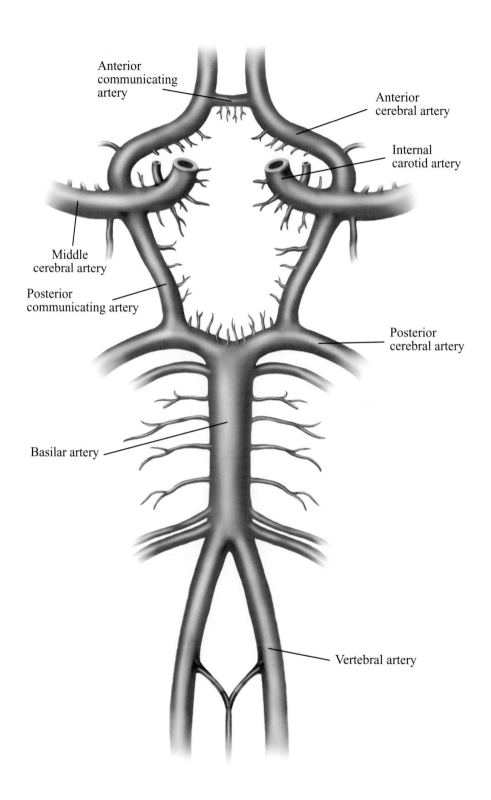

Anterior
communicating
artery

Anterior
cerebral artery

Internal
carotid artery

Middle
cerebral artery

Posterior
communicating artery

Posterior
cerebral artery

Basilar artery

Vertebral artery

Figure 49– The Circle of Willis

150

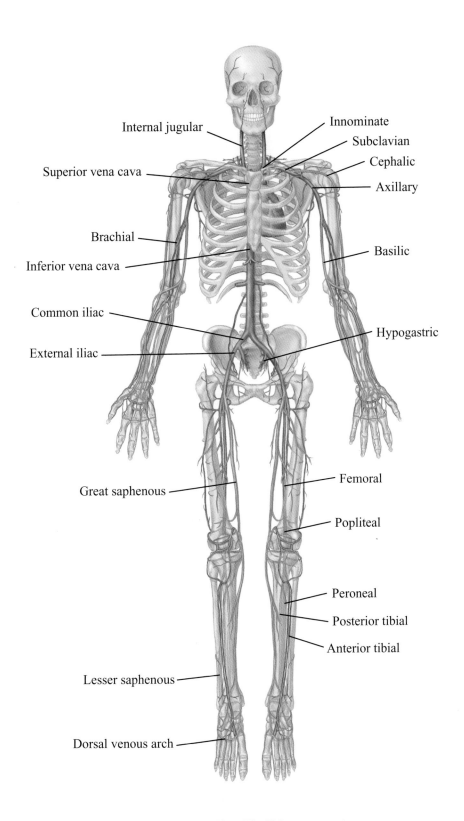

Internal jugular

Innominate

Subclavian

Cephalic

Superior vena cava

Axillary

Brachial

Basilic

Inferior vena cava

Common iliac

Hypogastric

External iliac

Femoral

Great saphenous

Popliteal

Peroneal

Posterior tibial

Anterior tibial

Lesser saphenous

Dorsal venous arch

Figure 50 – The Veins

151

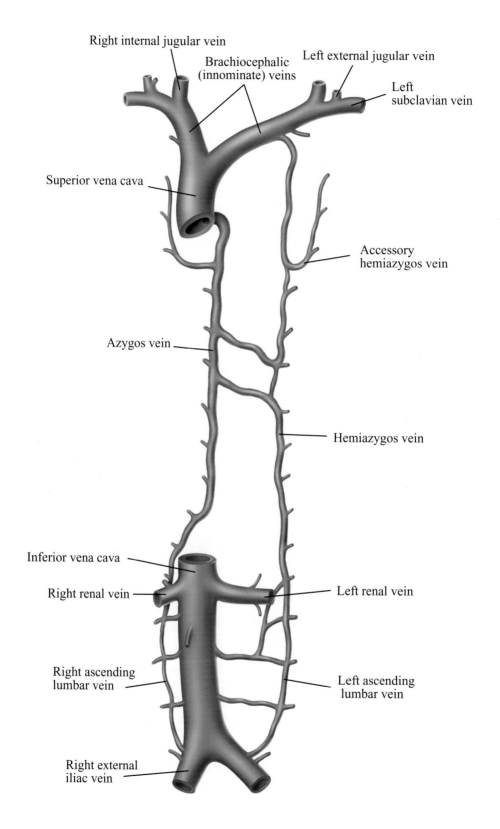

Right internal jugular vein

Brachiocephalic
(innominate) veins

Left external jugular vein

Left
subclavian vein

Superior vena cava

Accessory
hemiazygos vein

Azygos vein

Hemiazygos vein

Inferior vena cava

Right renal vein

Left renal vein

Right ascending
lumbar vein

Left ascending
lumbar vein

Right external
iliac vein

Figure 51– The Azygoes System

152

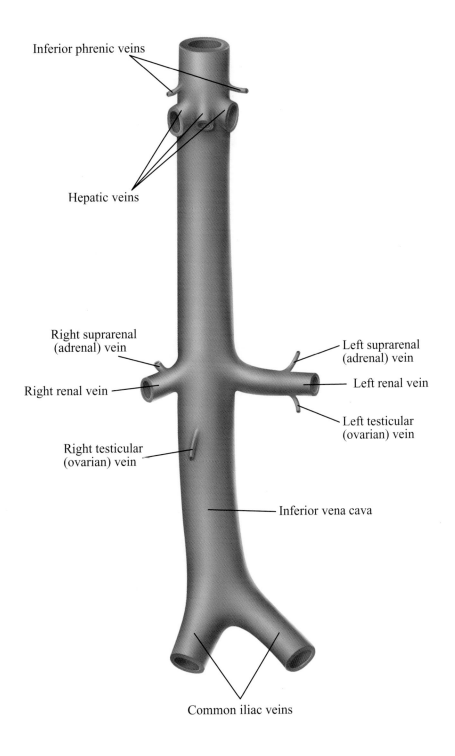

Inferior phrenic veins

Hepatic veins

Right suprarenal
(adrenal) vein

Right renal vein

Right testicular
(ovarian) vein

Left suprarenal
(adrenal) vein

Left renal vein

Left testicular
(ovarian) vein

Inferior vena cava

Common iliac veins

Figure 52– The Inferior Vena Cava

153

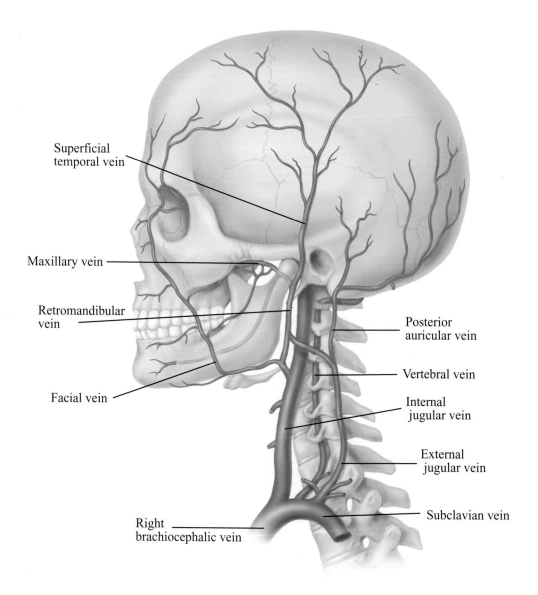

Superficial
temporal vein

Maxillary vein

Retromandibular
vein

Facial vein

Posterior
auricular vein

Vertebral vein

Internal
jugular vein

External
jugular vein

Subclavian vein

Right
brachiocephalic vein

Figure 53– Veins of the Head and Neck

154

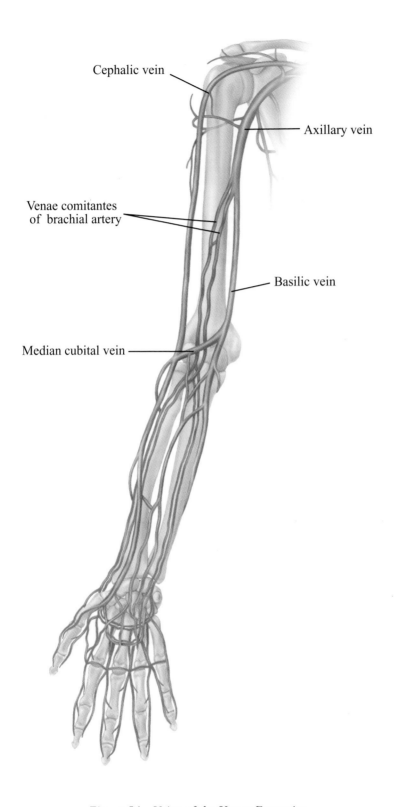

Cephalic vein

Axillary vein

Venae comitantes
of brachial artery

Basilic vein

Median cubital vein

Figure 54– Veins of the Upper Extremity

155

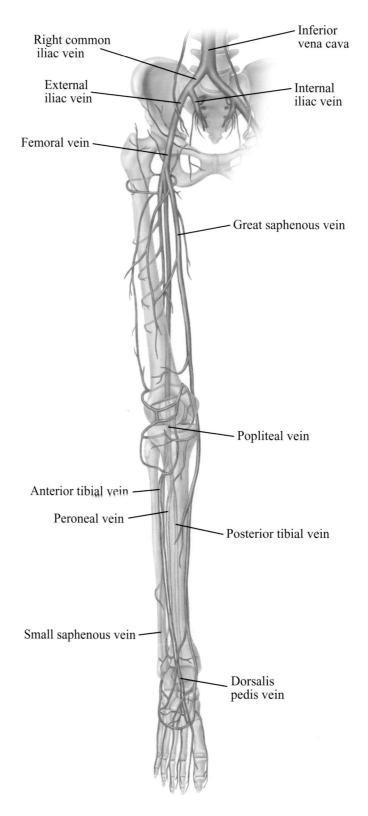

Right common
iliac vein

Inferior
vena cava

External
iliac vein

Internal
iliac vein

Femoral vein

Great saphenous vein

Popliteal vein

Anterior tibial vein

Peroneal vein

Posterior tibial vein

Small saphenous vein

Dorsalis
pedis vein

Figure 55– Veins of the Lower Extremity

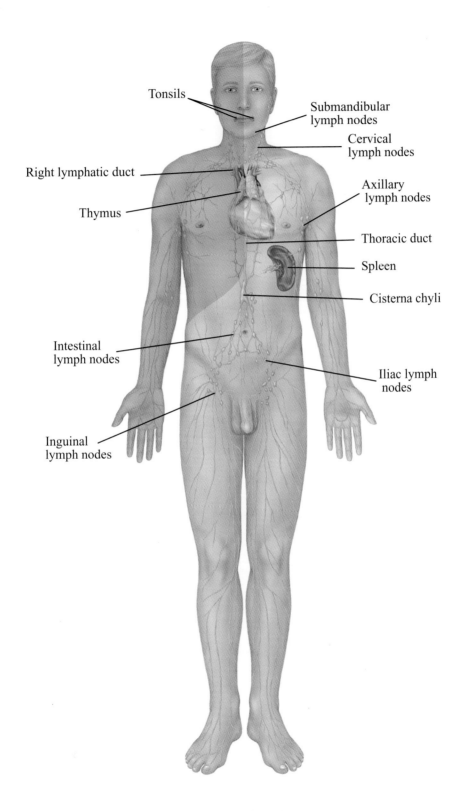

Tonsils

Submandibular
lymph nodes

Cervical
lymph nodes

Right lymphatic duct

Thymus

Axillary
lymph nodes

Thoracic duct

Spleen

Cisterna chyli

Intestinal
lymph nodes

Iliac lymph
nodes

Inguinal
lymph nodes

Figure 56– The Lymphatic System

157

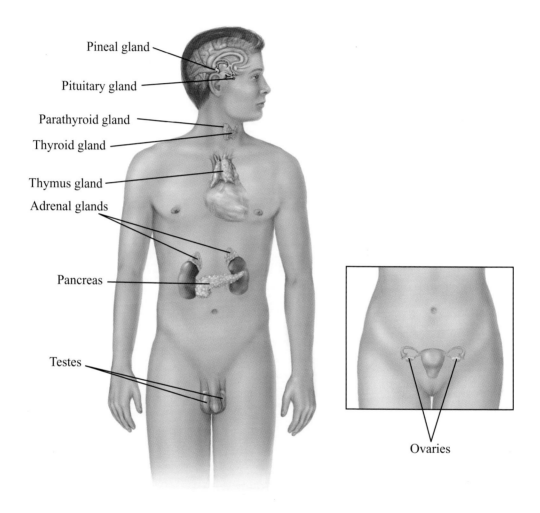

Pineal gland

Pituitary gland

Parathyroid gland

Thyroid gland

Thymus gland

Adrenal glands

Pancreas

Testes

Ovaries

Figure 57– The Endocrine System

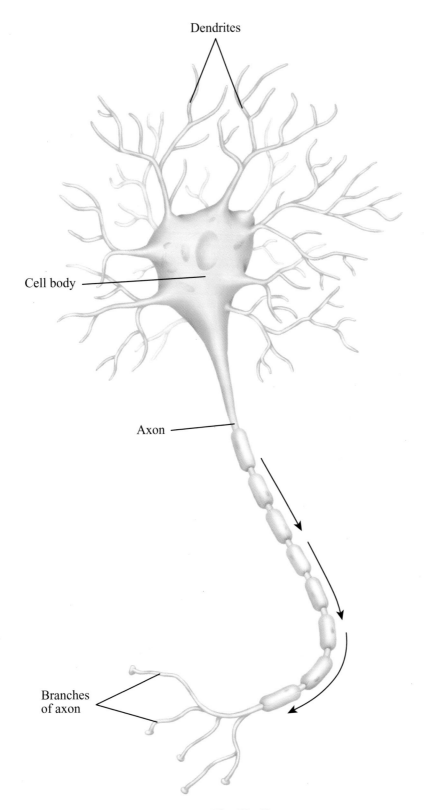

Dendrites

Cell body

Axon

Branches
of axon

Figure 58– The Nevron

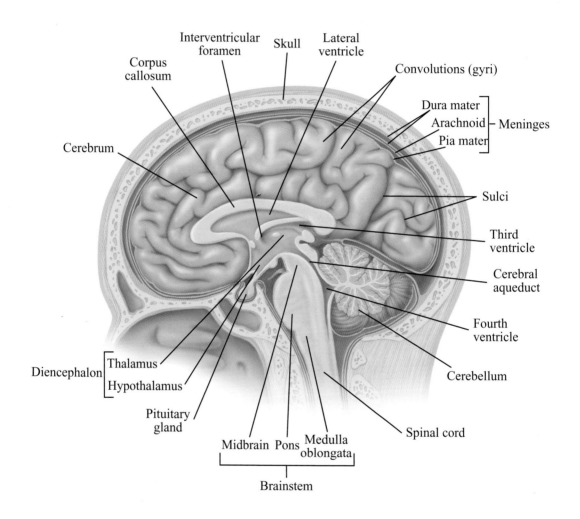

Corpus
callosum

Interventricular
foramen

Skull

Lateral
ventricle

Convolutions (gyri)

Dura mater
Arachnoid — Meninges
Pia mater

Cerebrum

Sulci

Third
ventricle

Cerebral
aqueduct

Fourth
ventricle

Cerebellum

Diencephalon
Thalamus
Hypothalamus

Pituitary
gland

Midbrain Pons Medulla
oblongata

Spinal cord

Brainstem

Figure 59– The Brain – Cross Section Veins

160